VOLUME 5

◁ **COVER PHOTOGRAPH**
Crab spider. (Page 535)
*Having selected a flower on which its own colour
will not be noticed, it seizes an unsuspecting fly.*

FRONTISPIECE ▷
Dik-Dik. (Page 610)
*Shy and elusive, they readily take to the under-
growth to hide.*

FUNK & WAGNALLS WILDLIFE ENCYCLOPEDIA

GENERAL EDITORS • Dr. Maurice Burton and Robert Burton

Also published as The International Wildlife Encyclopedia and Encyclopedia of Animal Life.

Funk & Wagnalls, Inc., New York, New York

Conger

The conger is a stout-bodied marine eel, normally up to 4 – 5 ft long but may reach 9 ft or more and a weight of 100 lb. There is an unconfirmed weight for 1940 of 160 lb. The body is scaleless, brown to dark slate and the underside may be silvery. The colour varies according to the sea-bed; on a sandy bottom being more or less colourless, and dark on a gravel bottom or among rocks. The gill-openings are large and extend to the underside of the body. The mouth runs backwards to below the level of the eye and is armed with rows of sharp teeth, one row in the upper jaw being set so close together they form a cutting edge. The front pair of nostrils are tubular, each of the hind pair being opposite the centre of the front edge of the eye. The eyes are large, reminiscent of those of deep-sea fishes. The pectoral fins are fairly large, the pelvics are lacking. The dorsal fin begins from above the pectorals, is continuous along the back and runs into the anal fin.

Congers are often called conger-eels. This is unnecessary. The name is from the Latin congrus *meaning sea-eel.*

The conger lives off rocky coasts, in the north and south Atlantic, Mediterranean, Indian and Pacific Oceans, but is not found on the west coast of the Americas. It also lives in deeper water, down to 660 ft or more.

Graceful acrobat

The conger swims easily and gracefully. When cruising it is propelled largely by wave-like movements passing down the dorsal and anal fins, from the front backwards. At greater speeds the body moves in a serpentine, side-to-side undulation. Not uncommonly it turns on its side to swim by undulating movements of the body. When doing this at the surface it presents a series of humps rather like those of the legendary sea-serpent. It spends the day lying among rocks or in crevices, sometimes on its back, periodically yawning, an action probably connected with respiration rather than fatigue. Congers are given to somewhat lethargic 'acrobatics', remaining poised head-down, sometimes doing so at the surface with a third or more of the body sticking up vertically out of the water. Or they may contort the body into other odd postures, holding each position for a perceptible time.

No flesh refused

Congers are carnivorous, taking any animal food including carrion and even smaller congers. Crabs and lobsters are held in the mouth and battered against rocks before being swallowed. The voracity of congers can be judged by stories of men having fingers bitten off when sorting a catch in which a conger lies hidden, or having a finger seized when feeling in rock crevices and having to cut it off to avoid being held

DP Wilson

Congers are distinguished from freshwater eels by their complete lack of scales. Their powerful jaws have a formidable battery of teeth – and a vice-like grip. With jaws agape, they often lurk in rocky crevices waiting to slip out after their prey.

and drowned when the tide came in. There is a story of a conger biting off the heel of a fisherman's sea-boot.

Thin-headed larvae

Like the freshwater eel the conger spawns once and then dies. The congers of European Atlantic waters spawn near the Sargasso Sea at depths of 10 200 ft in late summer. There is another spawning ground in the Mediterranean. Before spawning congers stop feeding, become almost black with very much enlarged eyes, especially in the male, and then look like deep-sea fishes. The female lays 3 – 8 million eggs, each $\frac{1}{16}$ in. diameter. These float in the intermediate layers of the ocean but occasionally reach the surface.

The first eel larva, of the freshwater eel, was found in 1777 and named *Leptocephalus* (thin-head) by the Italian naturalist Scopoli, under the impression that it was a new kind of fish. The first conger larva was found in 1763 by William Morris, of Holyhead, but was not described until 1788, when the German scientist Johann Gmelin named it *Leptocephalus morrisii*. And it was not until 1864 that it was recognized to be the larval stage of the conger. Even then, Albert Gunther, distinguished ichthyologist, held that it was a kind of freak, a case of arrested development. In 1886, however, Yves Delage the French zoologist proved beyond doubt that *Leptocephalus morrisii* was a larval conger by watching a leptocephalus change into a young conger in an aquarium. Later in the 19th century the true nature of what are now called the leptocephali became more firmly established when the Italian naturalist Raffaele managed to keep eggs and larvae of five species of eel alive in aquaria.

The conger leptocephali lose their larval teeth, on reaching coastal waters after their journey across the Atlantic, and change into young eels. The body becomes rounded and

eel-like and its length drops from 5 to 3 in. Until they reach a length of 15 in. the young congers are a pale pink. After this they gradually take on the dark colour of the adult. When about 2 ft long they move down the continental shelf, and beyond, into water more than 600 ft deep, and spend most of their time on the bottom.

Tons of floating conger

Dr Frank Buckland, in his *Curiosities of Natural History,* has recorded the observations made during January and February, 1855, by a surgeon who lived at St Leonards on the southeast coast of England: 'During the intense cold, some few miles out at sea, *thousands* of conger-eels were found floating on the surface of the water. They could progress readily in any direction, but could not descend, and consequently fell an easy prey, the boatmen catching them by means of hooks on the end of a long stick. In this manner no less than *eighty tons* were captured, of all sizes, some being as much as six feet long, and of a surprising circumference. The greater part of them were sent to London per rail. One of them I opened, and found the air-vessel (that is, swimbladder) distended with air to the utmost, so as to completely close the valvular opening. It was this, evidently, that buoyed them up.'

class	**Pisces**
order	**Anguilliformes**
family	**Congridae**
genus & species	*Conger conger*

Return to the nest. Coots prefer to nest among beds of reeds and water plants.

HM Barnfather: Photo Res

Coot

Coots swim well in the water because they have developed on each toe lobed flaps which act as paddles; these leave the toes free, unlike the webbed feet of ducks, so the bird is also very nimble on land.

Coots also have a white shield on the forehead, an extension of the bill. In the horned coot of South America, the shield is replaced by wattles and a fleshy horn or caruncle. The 10 kinds of coot are members of the rail family which includes the corncrake and moorhen and is related to the cranes.

The main home of coots is in South America, where seven kinds are found, including the horned coot and the giant coot that live in lonely lakes high in the Andes. The other three coots are very similar. The American coot, with a grey plumage, is found from central Canada to Ecuador and Colombia, the common or European coot extends from the British Isles to Japan, and the barely distinguishable crested or knob-billed coot ranges from southern Spain, throughout Africa to Cape Town.

An aggressive diver

Outside the breeding season coots gather in flocks of hundreds or thousands. They are found on fairly large bodies of water, compared with the related moorhen which can be seen on small ponds and streams.

During the breeding season coots keep to beds of reeds and other water plants where they can be seen threading their way through the stems, the white frontal shield drawing attention to the slow nodding of the head that accompanies the paddling. Sometimes they come out of the cover and can be seen leisurely crossing the pond in a straight line, headed for another clump of reeds. When alarmed, they run across the water with wings beating, leaving a trail of splashes, to subside with a crash and disappear into cover. At other times they will dive, neatly upending and disappearing below the surface leaving scarcely a ripple. They are on record as staying under for 27 seconds and descending to 24 ft.

Coots are not noted for the power of their flight, being rarely seen in the air. Take-off is long and laborious as they taxi over the water, but once airborne coots are capable of sustained flight and they are known to migrate regularly between the British Isles and the Continent.

Aggressive quarrelling is a feature of the coots' life that has often been remarked on. Both in the winter flocks and during the breeding season when pairs defend their territories, coots can be seen fighting, sending up sheets of water but rarely coming to blows. The first sign of aggression is the adoption of an aggressive posture by one or both coots, with head down and wings arched. If one does not retreat they swim together then suddenly erupt into a water-throwing match like bathers at the seaside. They sit back on their tails and splash water over each other by beating with the wings and feet. The contest is usually over in a few seconds, after which one may retreat, hotly pursued by the other.

Weed-eaters

Coots eat mainly water plants, diving down and bringing up masses of weed which is eaten on the surface. They also come on land to eat grass and even acorns. This diet is supplemented by animal food, including small fish, tadpoles, water insects, molluscs and worms. Occasionally they raid the nests of black-headed gulls and grebes, piercing the eggs and sipping the contents, and sometimes ducklings have been killed.

Floating island nests

Typically, coots make their nests among the tall water plants around the margins of lakes, building up a mass of dead reeds, flags and other leaves often rising 1 ft above water level and having a slipway for easier access. If the water level rises more vegetation is added to keep the eggs dry. Other nests, such as those made by the giant coot, are floating platforms of vegetation sometimes anchored to the stems of living water plants, but the nearby horned coots build their nests on natural hummocks or even make their own. On one lake horned coots were found to be making their nests of vegetation on piles of stones up to 6 ft high and 13 ft in diameter. The piles never broke the surface of the lake but had 1–2 ft of vegetation on top. Further observation showed that the nests were actually made by the horned coots. Pebbles were collected from the lake shore or the lake bed and carried in the bill to the pile, but as stones 11 lb. in weight were found in the pile this cannot have been the only method of transport, but, as yet, no one has seen how the coots manage such heavy weights. As it is, the building of the pile must be a very arduous business, although it is used from year to year with more stones being added each season.

Coots lay from March onwards in the British Isles. Usually 6–9 eggs are laid, but there may be as many as 15. Both parents incubate and the eggs hatch in just over 3 weeks. At first the female broods them while the male brings food, but after a few days the chicks leave the nest, returning at night to be brooded.

At first the parents do not specifically recognise their own chicks but will accept old the chicks begin diving for their own food and the down changes to a uniform blackish colour, relieved by dirty-white throat and underparts.

There are two, or sometimes three, broods a year and the older chicks help their parents to raise the nest in times of flood and will bring food for the younger chicks.

Coots' aerial defence

Now that birds of prey are rare coots do not have many enemies but sea-eagles, hawks, especially harriers, and greater black-backed gulls prey on them. Outside the breeding season, when the coots are living on large stretches of open water, their defence is based on safety in numbers. They keep close together in large rafts that make it difficult for an enemy to single out any individual for attack. As the raft moves slowly forward, some coots get left behind feeding, but they soon rush to catch up the raft when the gap between them widens. Bunching together is a common method of defeating aerial enemies. Black-headed gulls, for example, fly around in tight formation when peregrines are sighted. Coots do much the same but on water.

Sometimes the coots' defence is more active. They have been seen to throw up a shower of spray in the face of a hawk as it swoops down on the flock. Considering the amount of spray sent up by a pair of coots when fighting, a flock must put up quite an effective barrage.

WM Scott

▽ *Coots have developed feet with lobed flaps on each toe, which make very efficient paddles.*

△ *Coot chicks are fed by the parents for one month, when they begin to fend for themselves*

WM Scott

and feed any chick about the same size as their own. Chicks considerably larger or smaller are, however, attacked and even killed if they do not retreat. Later, when their own chicks are about a fortnight old, the parents recognise them as individuals and no other chick is allowed in the territory. At the same time the chicks, which used to beg food from any adult, now solicit only from their parents.

The young chicks are clad in a sooty down but their heads are brilliantly coloured. Around the bill, which is white with a black tip and shading to vermilion on the frontal shield, is a patch of red down. The sides of the face are orange, the crown blue and the nape red, orange or black. When a month

class	**Aves**
order	**Gruiformes**
family	**Rallidae**
genus & species	***Fulica americana*** *American coot* ***F. atra*** *European coot* ***F. cornuta*** *horned coot* ***F. cristata*** *crested or knob-billed coot* ***F. gigantea*** *giant coot*

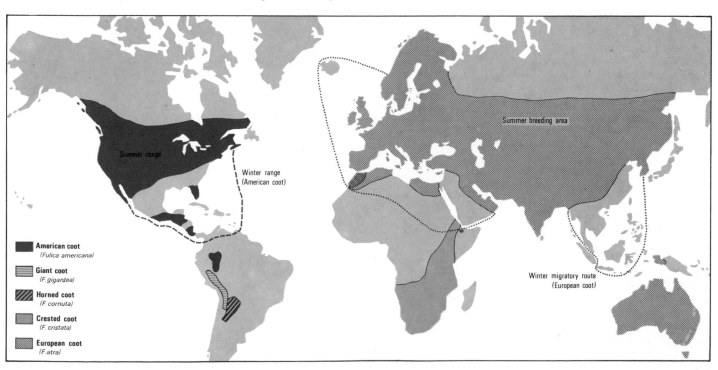

American coot
(*Fulica americana*)

Giant coot
(*F. gigantea*)

Horned coot
(*F. cornuta*)

Crested coot
(*F. cristata*)

European coot
(*F.atra*)

Summer range

Winter range
(American coot)

Summer breeding area

Winter migratory route
(European coot)

Copepod

Copepods are small, usually free-swimming crustaceans which occur in both freshwater and the sea where they form a major part of the plankton. Often coloured green, orange, blue or red, and rarely more than a ½ in. long, copepods have segmented bodies, covered with stiff bristles called setae. They have two pairs of antennae and many pairs of legs, some of which are used for feeding and some for swimming. Most have only one eye, coloured black or red, on top of the head. One of the best known freshwater copepods has been called Cyclops *because of this. In Greek mythology, the Cyclops were a group of one-eyed giants, the eye being in the middle of the forehead. Although all copepods, apart from a few which are parasitic, are basically much alike, they are divided into three orders:* Calanoida, Cyclopoida, *and* Harpacticoida. *The most striking difference between the three groups lies in the length of the antennae, which is longer than the body in the calanoids, about half body length in the cyclopoids, and very short in the harpacticoids.*

Many swimming styles

Free-swimming copepods are common in all freshwaters, particularly in stagnant ponds, and they may be active even in the depths of winter. *Cyclops* swims with the front pairs of legs on the underside of the body. It can also glide slowly by the action of the leg-like second pair of antennae on the head while the body limbs are held to the sides. Some copepods swim by alternately bending and straightening their bodies. These spend most of their time crawling about over algae or other aquatic vegetation. Larval copepods often move differently from the adults, in jerky rushes followed by a period of floating or free gliding. The larvae often seem particularly attracted to sunlight, frequenting the upper layers of water, whereas adults tend to live lower down.

The long antennae of free-swimming copepods are ornamented with bristles which help to keep them poised in water. They would, however, gradually sink but for the beating of the shorter second pair of antennae, that drive them up. When the copepod needs to put on a spurt, the swimming legs on the underside of the body come into play.

Feeders on particles

There are many different ways of feeding among copepods. Some eat tiny floating plants, such as diatoms and algae. Others filter small particles of food from the water with a complex sieving mechanism, the limbs around the mouth setting up a continuous 'flickering' or pulsating movement which drives water through the sieve. The various species of *Cyclops* are able to capture and eat relatively large animals, and are also said to eat decaying matter. A number of the Cyclopoida, which are mainly marine, are parasitic on certain fish, such as salmon. They are found on the inside of the gill covers where they suck the fish's blood.

All eggs not in one basket

Mating and egg production may take place at any time of the year. The female, usually bigger than the male, lays her eggs in an egg-sac, while *Cyclops* always has two, one either side of its abdomen. A few lay their eggs straight into the water.

Many freshwater copepods have evolved ways to avoid the effects of unfavourable conditions, such as excessive cold or drought, by producing two different types of egg. One kind develops rapidly and hatches in about 10 days, while the other, larger and more resistant to cold or drought, lies on the bottom of the pool or lake, and may take many weeks to develop. It is probably through these that copepods are dispersed, the eggs becoming attached to the muddy

Female Cyclops *or water-flea, showing the large egg-sacs (150 × life size).*

Nauplius larva (250 × life size).

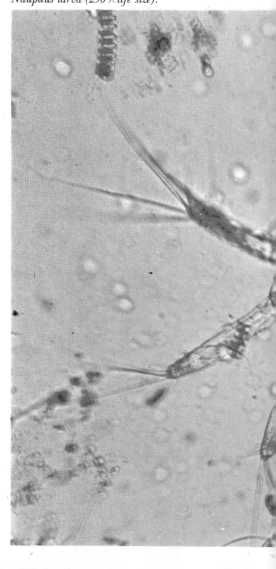

Peter Parks

feet of aquatic birds and thus carried from one stretch of water to another.

When they emerge, the larvae, called nauplii, are quite unlike their parents, being rounded and with only a few pairs of limbs. They are extremely small, and difficult to pick out in a sample of water, although their single dark coloured eye is often a means of pin-pointing them. With each moult, the larva increases in size and shows more adult characters. After six moults, the so-called Copepodid stage is reached. Then follows a further series of moults, with corresponding growth, until the adult stage is reached.

Male marine copepods fertilise the female by making a kind of microscopic plastic bottle with a long neck. Into this they shed their sperms, seize a female with a kind of clasp-knife joint on one of their antennae, then fasten the flask of sperms to her body.

The rate of development of the larvae depends to a large extent on the temperature of the water and the amount of food available. Copepods attain their densest populations when the quicker emerging eggs are being produced. Whether this is in summer or winter depends on the species concerned and the external conditions.

Enemies

Copepods form the food of a variety of fish. Free-swimming ones are sometimes the intermediate hosts for certain parasitic worms. The parasitic larvae living within the crustacean cannot complete their development until eaten by a fish, in which the life cycle is completed.

Cold and drought are also likely to harm populations, although some species may encyst and spend long periods hibernating through the winter or aestivating during the hotter parts of summer. Certain forms of marine copepods can give off clouds of luminescence, which may be a means of warding off predators.

Unreapable harvest?

By far the most numerous and most important of copepods are the marine forms, especially *Calanus*. These are very like *Cyclops* in form and way of life. Sir Alastair Hardy, in his book *Plankton*, draws attention to the abundance of copepods in one haul with a tow-net. He then remarks that if we realize that such numbers are stretching through the waters of the vast oceans for thousands of miles in every direction, then we must recognize that for sheer abundance the Copepoda have first place. Herring, as we shall later see, exist in astronomical numbers, and they feed on *Calanus finmarchicus*, a copepod occurring in such vast numbers as to colour the sea, although each is only the size of a rice grain.

It is this overwhelming abundance that has given rise to so much talk about using plankton for feeding the world's expanding human populations. Hardy has something to say on this also. *Calanus finmarchicus*, very like *Cyclops* in shape, is transparent, with scarlet tinges over the body and its egg-sacs bright blue. He fried some of these beautiful 'rice grains' in butter and served them on toast, and found them delicious.

Hardy also tried experiments using large nets swinging in the tidal flow of Scottish sea lochs. The amount of plankton he caught was not worth the effort. So until some means is found of economically harvesting this vast resource all we shall have will be scarlet-and-blue 'rice grains' on toast for the gourmet.

phylum	**Arthropoda**
class	**Crustacea**
subclass	**Copepoda**
orders	**Calanoida, Cyclopoida, Harpacticoida**
genera	*Cyclops, Calanus* others

A swarm of Caligus zei *(fish-lice) on the side of a John Dory seafish (5½ × life size).*

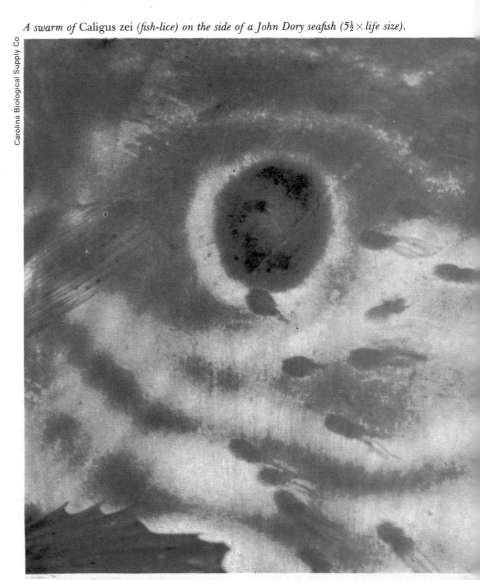

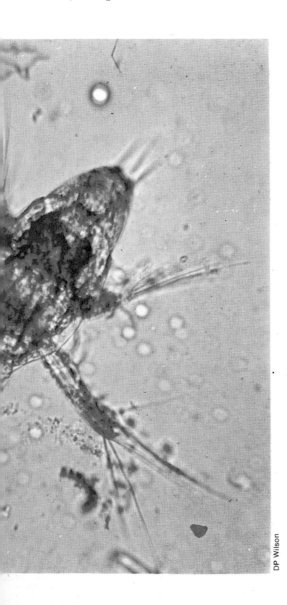

Copper butterfly

The wings of these butterflies have the colour and lustre of polished copper and are marked with dark spots and bands, sometimes with blue or purple as well. They are a group of small butterflies in the family Lycaenidae, and are thus allied to the blues and hairstreaks. They are widely distributed in the temperate and cold regions of the northern hemisphere, both in the Old and the New World. There are, however, three species in temperate New Zealand. Presumably their ancestors arose from the same stock as those in the northern hemisphere and in time became separated.

The caterpillars are slug-shaped and, in the majority of species, feed on various kinds of dock or sorrel. Like those of many of the blues (see p 245) the larvae of some species are attended by ants for the sake of a sweet secretion which they produce. In the case of the coppers this exudes all over the body, unlike many others of the family, which have a single orifice connected with a special gland.

Two species are associated with Britain, one as a familiar butterfly of fields; downland and open country in general, the other as an insect which unhappily became extinct quite recently. They are known respectively as the small copper and the large copper.

Small copper

This is a pretty, lively and even rather aggressive little butterfly. The males establish territories and try to chase all other butterflies away, flying out and attacking individuals of their own species and other, larger ones as well. They have no weapons and are quite incapable of injuring each other.

The small copper is found all over the British Isles and has an enormous range extending from Europe right across Asia to Japan, over a large part of North America and northward to beyond the Arctic Circle. It is divided into distinct subspecies in different parts of its range but they are all very similar in appearance. Some of these subspecies range into Africa. Another ranges almost as far north as any butterfly, into Ellesmere Land, and is one of the five butterflies found in Greenland.

Three generations a year

The larva feeds on dock and sorrel and the life cycle is passed through so quickly that there may be three generations in a good summer. The caterpillar is green with a brown line along the back and clothed with short greyish hairs. It is not attended by ants. The pupa is pale brown or greenish and attached to a leaf or stem of the food plant. The species overwinters as a larva but not (as in most larval hibernators) at any particular stage of its growth. The butterfly is on the wing continuously from May to October.

The small copper is exceedingly variable, and its more extreme varieties or 'aberrations' are eagerly sought by collectors. Re-

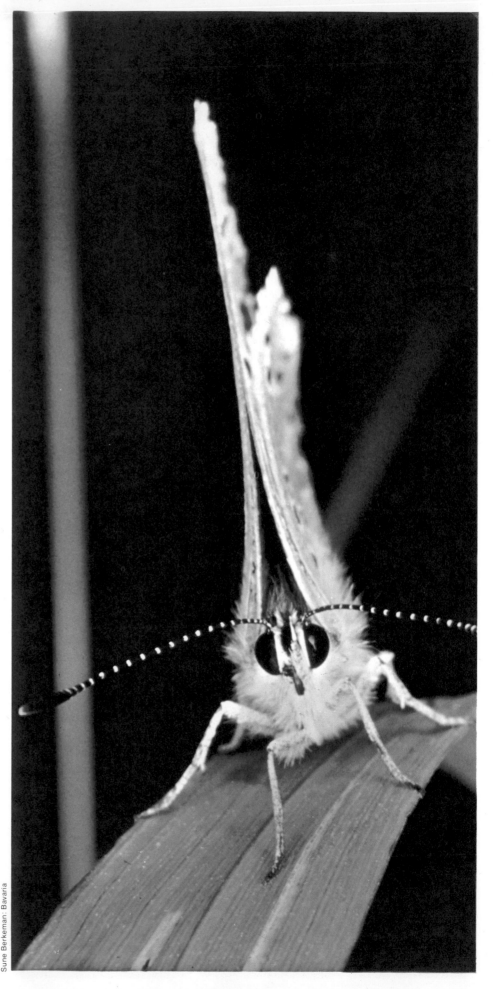

Sune Berkeman: Bavaria

502

Jane Burton: Photo Res

◁ *Small copper at rest. These far-ranging butterflies often breed three times a year.*

△ *A small copper shows its wing pattern while taking a meal off a sprig of heather.*

▽ *One of the Dutch large coppers introduced to Wood Walton Fen on great water dock plant.*

by ants, is green and looks like a much flattened slug. It hibernates when young, feeds in the following spring, and the butterflies appear in July and August.

Two other species, the scarce copper and the purple-edged copper, were included as British by early entomologists. It is not impossible that they once lived in this country and became extinct before collecting became methodical and widespread. Both are well distributed in continental Europe. One or two allegedly British specimens of the scarce copper still exist.

Butterfly naturalisation

In 1915 a subspecies of the large copper was discovered in the province of Friesland, Holland, and named *Lycaena dispar batavus*. It resembles the extinct English race more closely than any other and the idea occurred to some British naturalists to try introducing it to the fenland nature reserves in East Anglia. It is rare in its native haunts, and some difficulty was experienced in obtaining living specimens. This was overcome, however, and the first butterflies were released by the Society for the Promotion of Nature Reserves in Wood Walton Fen, Huntingdonshire, in 1927. The experiment was successful and later was repeated at

duction or modification of the pattern of black bands and spots produces most of the varieties, but in one of the rarest and most highly prized the copper ground colour is replaced by silvery white.

Large copper

In this species the wing span is about $1\frac{7}{10}$ in. and the male and female are very different. In the male all four wings on the upper side are brilliant burnished copper with only narrow dark borders and small central dots. The female has dark markings not unlike those of the small copper.

The large copper was discovered in Britain a little before 1800, in the fens of East Anglia, a habitat that was rapidly shrinking due to artificial drainage. Butterfly collecting was already a popular pastime, and the coppers were persecuted without restraint. Not only did collectors visit their haunts, but dealers encouraged the local people to capture them in all their stages for sale at prices ranging from a few pence to a shilling, rich rewards for the poor of those days. The butterfly held out for half a cen-

Small copper larvae feed on dock and sorrel.

PH Ward

tury, the last specimens being taken in 1847 or 1848. The British large copper could probably have been saved if a reserve had been created where it could have been secure from the greed of collectors and from destruction of its habitat, but at that time the idea had not occurred to anyone that active measures might be taken to preserve rare animals from extinction.

The large copper is still found in many parts of Europe and Asia, but the British subspecies was larger and finer than any of the Continental forms. About a thousand preserved specimens of it exist, but as a living animal it has gone for ever. The great water dock is the food plant of the large copper. The caterpillar, which is attended

Joyce Pope

Wicken Fen, owned by the National Trust, in Cambridgeshire. The Dutch large copper is still maintained at Wood Walton and is bred artificially and released every year to supplement wild stock and to ensure against any accident to the small wild population.

phylum	**Arthropoda**
class	**Insecta**
order	**Lepidoptera**
family	**Lycaenidae**
genus & species	*Lycaena dispar* large copper *L. hippothoe* purple-edged copper *L. phlaeas* small copper *L. virgauteae* scarce copper

503

Coral

Corals are polyps similar to anemones (see p 44) except that they are supported by a hard chalky skeleton. This, often white when dead, is covered in life with a continuous layer of flesh from which the polyps spring, and the whole is often beautifully coloured. The true corals, or stony corals as they are often called, may be either solitary or colonial. In the first a single polyp lives on its own, seated in a chalky cup or on a mush-room-shaped chalky skeleton. The colonial corals are made up of a sheet of tissue, formed by hundreds or thousands of polyps, covering the chalky skeleton. They may be tree-, cup- or dome-shaped, made up of flattened plates or branching like stag's horns.

There are also soft corals, some of which are precious. They are not true corals. One important difference is that their tentacles, instead of being simple as in the true corals and sea-anemones, are fringed, and each polyp has eight tentacles instead of, as in true corals, six or some multiple of six. Soft corals are usually tree-like and the centres of the stems and branches are strengthened by a chalky material, coloured red or black, and this, stripped of its flesh, gives the precious corals of commerce. Related to the precious corals are the sea-fans, the stems and branches of which are strengthened by a flexible horny material. Another relative is the beautiful organ-pipe coral, a mass of vertical tubes joined at intervals throughout their length by thin horizontal plates. The skeleton is reddish-purple and the polyps a pale lilac. When expanded these look like delicate flowers.

Tropical reef builders

Corals live in all seas, but few are found in temperate and polar regions compared with those found in the tropics—and in particular the reef-builders. Thousands of miles of tropical shores, especially in the Indian Ocean, are edged with reefs. In places, barrier reefs are formed, many miles off-shore, like the Great Barrier Reef, which runs for 1 200 miles parallel with the northeast coast of Australia. In mid-ocean, especially in the Pacific, are ring-shaped atolls made of living coral, topping accumulations of dead coral skeletons, which in places go down to about a mile deep.

Birth of a reef

Reef-building corals are found north and south of the equator about as far as the 25th line of latitude, where the temperature of the sea does not fall much below 18°C/65°F. Each begins as a larva which, after swimming about for a while, settles on the bottom and changes into a polyp. A small lump appears on its side. This is a bud. It gets bigger, a mouth appears at its free end and a crown of tentacles grows around the mouth. The bud then continues to grow until it is the same size and shape as the

parent, but without becoming separated from it. By repeated budding of the parent stock, and of the new growths formed from it, a colony numbering sometimes hundreds of thousands is formed. Between them they build a common skeleton, which in the end may be several feet high and the same across. Since all the polyps are in close connection with each other they are fed communally by their many mouths and stomachs.

Living animal traps

Corals, whether solitary, reef or soft, feed like sea-anemones. The tentacles are armed with stinging cells by which small swimming animals are paralysed and then pushed into the mouth at the centre of the ring of tentacles. In reef corals the polyps are withdrawn during the day, so the surface of each coral mass is more or less smooth. As night falls and the plankton animals rise into the surface waters, the polyps and their tentacles become swollen with water drawn in through the mouth by currents set up by cilia on the skin. The polyps now stand out on the surface, their delicate tentacles forming a semi-transparent pile in which are many mouths, waiting to receive prey. The seemingly inert coral has been converted into a huge trap for any small animals which pass nearby—underlining the relationship with anemones.

The polyps of some corals have short tentacles, which do not carry food to the mouth. Instead, it is passed to the mouth by the cilia coating the tentacles.

There has always been some doubt, however, whether this was their only method of feeding. In coral tissues live microscopic single-celled plants known as zooxanthellae. It has been supposed that these two, the polyps and the zooxanthellae, were living in symbiosis: that the zooxanthellae received shelter and used the waste products from the coral, while the coral benefited from oxygen given off by its plant guests. Some scientists maintained that in addition the coral fed on the surplus populations of the plants.

This has been disputed, and one reason why it was hard to reach the truth is that digestion is very rapid. Consequently no animal food is found in the coral stomachs by day, therefore it has been assumed that they must be feeding on something else and, so it was argued, they must be eating the zooxanthellae. On the other hand, the tentacles react to animal food only, suggesting that corals are wholly carnivorous. Moreover, if coral polyps are deprived of animal food they soon shrink, showing signs of malnutrition. These are only a few of the arguments and they are enough to indicate the causes of disagreement.

From investigations carried out about 1960 by TF Goreau in the West Indies it seems that the zooxanthellae help the corals to grow by removing carbon dioxide from their tissues. Corals grow best in bright light, less well in dull light when zooxanthellae are fewer, and least of all in darkness when their zooxanthellae have been killed off by lack of sunlight. This alone suggests that there is a close link between the rate of growth of the coral and the presence of tiny plants in its tissues.

Walking corals

The majority of corals are sedentary. The original meaning of this word is 'to sit for long periods', but in zoology it is used more to indicate animals that are permanently fixed to the substratum. There is, however, at least one coral that moves about, but it does not travel under its own steam. It represents a very picturesque example of symbiosis, or living together for mutual benefit.

In October 1967, TF Goreau and Sir Maurice Yonge were exploring the Great Barrier Reef of Australia when they discovered on the lee side of the reef, on a muddy bottom, small corals, less than an inch across, which moved about over the mud. They were able to take some to the laboratory and watch them in an aquarium.

The coral *Heteropsammia michelinii* is solitary, with usually one polyp seated on the limy base, although sometimes there may be two or even three polyps on the same base. This coral belongs to the same kind as those that form the reefs, but its limy skeleton contains a cavity and in the cavity lives a marine worm. The worm drives its head into the mud to extract edible particles from it, in the usual manner of a worm, but as it feeds it travels along dragging the coral with it.

phylum	**Coelenterata**
class	**Anthozoa**
order	**Scleractinia**
genera	***Fungia, Porites, Heteropsammia*** *others*

▷ *Four examples of dead coral colonies show how they are made up of skeletal frameworks of individual polyps. In life, these skeletons are covered with beautifully-coloured layers of living flesh (see overleaf).*

▽ *Diagram of the basic colony of the* Heliopora *blue coral shows the shape of the hard, chalky skeleton (in red) and the polyps which grow from it (top).*

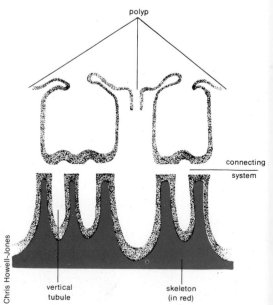

polyp

connecting system

vertical tubule

skeleton (in red)

Chris Howell-Jones

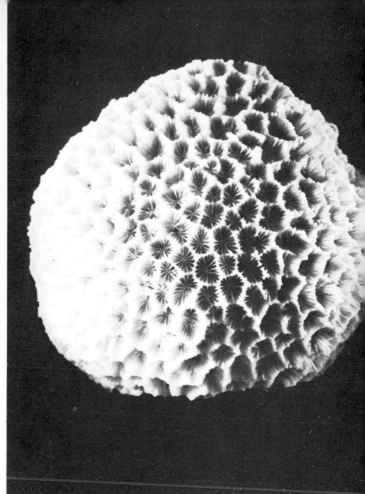
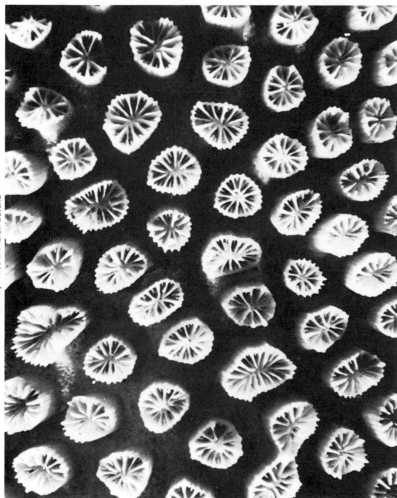

◁ *This assortment gives a good idea of the different types of coral which will grow side by side to form a coral reef.*

G Mundey

Helmut Stellrecht

Anthony Bannister: NHPA

△ *All systems 'go': the polyps of a coral, fully extended while feeding at night.*

◁ *A closer view of feeding polyps of a hard coral show the fine, whiskery tentacles that sweep the surrounding water for food.*

▷ Living polyps protrude from branches of staghorn coral off Mauritius.

▷▷ Unidentified shallow-water coral in the Seychelles has a squat, bunched structure.

Anthony Bannister: NHPA

Anthony Bannister: NHPA

▷ Fish swarm around a coral reef precipice in the Red Sea.

G Mundey

Coral snake

Coral snake is the name given to many strikingly-coloured snakes with patterns of rings running round the body and tail. The body is slender, and there is no pronounced distinction between head and neck, as in the vipers. In North and South America there are several genera of true coral snakes, which are close relatives of the cobras, as are the Oriental coral snakes belonging to the genus Maticora. *In South Africa some members of the genus* Aspidelaps *are called coral snakes, and they are very similar in appearance and habits to their American relatives.*

The two North American coral snakes have prominent rings round the body in the same sequence of black, yellow or white, and red. The Arizona or Sonora coral snake is small, having a maximum recorded length of $19\frac{1}{2}$ in. The larger common coral snake occasionally reaches over $3\frac{1}{2}$ ft. Some tropical species reach 4 or 5 ft.

Brightly-coloured banding is not in-

Technicolor warning technique. Bright colours do for the coral what the dry, sinister rattle does for the rattlesnake: they warn potential attackers not to try their luck.

variable in coral snakes. The genus Leptomicrurus *has long thin bodies and short tails, which are dark on the upper side and have yellow spots underneath.*

Of the many species of New World coral snakes, only two extend as far north as the United States. The common coral snake extends north from Mexico, through eastern Texas to the low-lying country of Kentucky and North Carolina and south to Florida. The Arizona coral snake lives in the arid lands of Arizona, New Mexico and northern Mexico. Other coral snakes range south to northern Argentina.

Poisonous but rarely dangerous

Coral snakes do not strike like a cobra, but approach their victim slowly, sliding their head over its flesh. The fangs are short and to inject a lethal quantity of venom the snake chews the flesh, lacerating the skin and so forcing in a large amount of poison, which acts on the nervous system and has a very powerful effect. In Mexico the common coral snake is called the '20-minute snake' as its bite is supposed to be fatal within that time. But 24 hours is a more likely time. Surprisingly few deaths have been reported.

Coral snakes are nocturnal, lying up during the day in runs under stones or bark or in mossy clumps, but they are sometimes active during the day if it has been raining. They trouble people little because of their secretive habits. When man is abroad during the day, coral snakes are resting away from the danger of being trodden on, which would cause them to bite. Occasionally there are reports of coral snake bites but these are usually due to people carelessly handling them.

Snake eaters

The jaws of coral snakes do not open very wide and they can eat only slender prey, which consists mainly of small lizards, other snakes and probably insects.

Breeding

The common coral snake lays 3–14 soft, elongated eggs in May or June, in a hollow in the earth or under a log. When they hatch, after 10–12 weeks, the young snakes measure 7–8 in. and have pale skins, the colours of which become more intense as they get older.

Enemies

Snake-eaters themselves, coral snakes are preyed upon by other snake-eaters such as the king snake, which is resistant to the effects of coral snake venom. On Trinidad, mongooses, which were introduced to keep down the numbers of snakes, have not affected the coral snake population.

One unusual report is that of a large bullfrog eating a 17in. coral snake. Although the narrow-jawed snake could not have swallowed the bullfrog, it is strange that it was not able either to escape or to poison its adversary.

First-class animal puzzle

Parallels can be drawn between the brightly-coloured coral snake, perhaps the most gaudy of animals, apart from some of the birds and fishes, and the bright stripes of bees and wasps. Conspicuous colouring is a feature of many animals that are poisonous, whether the poison is transmitted by stings, fangs or merely by being set free when the body is eaten, as in the burnet moth.

In the insect world, some harmless insects, such as hoverflies, mimic the colour patterns of the harmful bees and wasps, gaining protection because birds and other predators learn to connect the colour with an unpleasant taste. It is suggested that the coral snakes also have their mimics, for in America, Africa and Asia there are non-poisonous snakes with brightly-coloured rings. In the United States some reports of coral snakes in unusual places have been due to two non-poisonous snakes, the scarlet snake and the scarlet king snake. These, however, have a different sequence of bands. In the coral snakes the red band has yellow or white on either side. In the mimics the red band has a black band on either side. This is put another way by Drs Boys and Smith in their book on recognising poisonous amphibians and reptiles and treating their bites:

'Red on yellow (or white)
Kill a fellow (or might);
Red on black
Venom lack'

This distinction does not hold elsewhere in America. The false coral snake of South America has no yellow bands.

The trouble with the theory of the coral snake's bright colours being a warning is that it is nocturnal, so enemies are unlikely to see the colour and therefore are unlikely to learn that a bright-banded snake is dangerous. How then are the mimicking snakes, who are also secretive, to profit? One habit shared by many ringed snakes, both venomous and harmless, is to coil themselves up with the head underneath and wave the tail, which looks rather like the head in these species. Perhaps this leads an enemy to attack a less vulnerable part of the snake. However, one animal who does notice bright colour is man, and because he will kill any snake that might be poisonous, the harmless mimics actually suffer from looking like a venomous snake.

class	**Reptilia**
order	**Squamata**
suborder	**Serpentes**
family	**Elapidae**
genera	*Microides*
	Micrurus
	Leptomicrurus
	others

John Tashjian at Fort Worth Zoo

508

Cormorant

Cormorant and shag are names applied indiscriminately to the 30 species of the family Phalacrocoracidae. Only in the British Isles does each name refer to a certain species, where cormorant describes the common cormorant, and shag the green cormorant. The common cormorant, the largest of all, is also known as the great cormorant in North America and the black cormorant in Australia and New Zealand. The plumage is generally glossy black with some bronze and an overall greyish appearance to the head and neck due to some greyish-white feathers. There is a characteristic white patch on the chin and sides of the face. The shag has a glossy bottle-green plumage and is distinguished from the common cormorant by the absence of white on the head and by having a small, curved crest during the breeding season, which is, however, a feature of many other members of the family.

The various species of cormorant are best identified by the shape and colouring of the patch of naked skin on the face, although these variations can only be detected at close quarters. Brandt's cormorant, the commonest species on the Pacific coast of North America, has blue patches, and the double-crested cormorant, the commonest elsewhere in North America, has orange-yellow patches. The face patches of the Magellan cormorant are red. Many of the species living in the southern hemisphere have white, rather than mainly dark, underparts.

Cosmopolitan swimmers

Cormorants are found all over the world except on the islands of the central Pacific. The pelagic cormorant is found in the Bering Sea, while, to the south, the blue-eyed shag, named for its ultramarine eyes surrounded by rings of blue naked skin, breeds on islands off the west coast of the Antarctic Peninsula.

Although the webbed feet, upright stance and long neck all suggest an aquatic life, cormorants are rarely found far out to sea. Most of them live by shallow coastal waters, or inland on lakes and rivers. The most cosmopolitan species is the common cormorant which is found over most of Europe, Asia, Africa, Australasia and eastern North America. The most restricted is the flightless cormorant that breeds on two islands only of the Galapagos. This is one of the largest cormorants. It has completely lost the power of flight and has paralleled the penguins in its flipper-like wings and dense hair-like plumage. Another cormorant that could fly only weakly was Pallas' cormorant which was discovered on the Komandorski Islands by Steller and Bering when they were marooned there in 1741. A century later it was extinct.

Other cormorants are strong fliers, keeping aloft on rapid wingbeats with neck stretched out. They will also soar in air currents, but usually they fly low over the

△ *An obliging duo show both the cormorant's basic streamline and its characteristic stance.*

▽ *A mixed bag. Cormorants share a nesting site with a group of sacred ibis.*

Stephen Dalton: NHPA

Des Bartlett: Photo Res

509

Two generations—fledgeling and adult blue-eyed shags in southern waters, with nesting chinstrap penguins.

surface of the water. All of them swim well, floating low in the water, sometimes with only head and neck showing. To submerge, they either duck-dive, jumping up and plunging in head-first, or merely sink beneath the surface. The longest recorded dive is of 71 seconds and cormorants may go down as far as 100 ft. Normally they stay under for less than half a minute, swimming about 20—30 ft below the surface.

Fishing in flocks

Except for a few crustaceans, such as crabs, molluscs and occasionally frogs and reptiles, cormorants feed on fish. The flightless cormorant feeds on octopus and fish, mainly eels, which it finds in great numbers around its home islands, where the cool Humboldt current wells up and mixes with the warm equatorial waters to form a fertile area with an abundance of plankton and fish.

The British cormorant and shag have slightly different diets. The cormorant feeds mainly on bottom-living fish such as flat fish and sand eels while the shag eats eels and fish from the middle and upper waters. In this way the two closely-related species that nest on the same cliffs, and fish in the same waters, do not compete for food.

Flocks of cormorants go out feeding together. They can be seen flying in lines then settling on the water, gathering in a tight bunch. They swim about, lowering their heads into the water to look for fish, then one dives and the others follow it. Flocks of little black cormorants are reported to locate shoals of fish then swim round them in decreasing circles to concentrate them and double-crested cormorants have been seen driving shoals of fish up a bay into shallower water.

Fish are brought to the surface, to be

swallowed head first. Large fish are shaken or beaten against the water until their struggles weaken. This habit has been used by Japanese fishermen, who train cormorants to bring their catch back to the boat. Leather collars are used to prevent the cormorants from swallowing the catch.

Other fishermen persecute the cormorant for its fish-eating habits, but the cormorants' gluttony has given rise to an important industry. The guanay of Peru and Chile and the cape cormorant of South Africa feed in vast numbers, and their droppings, deposited on the breeding grounds, form guano. This is dug out and used as a very rich fertilizer.

Nesting on rocks and in trees

Cormorants nest in colonies varying from a few pairs, perhaps only one or two in the case of the king cormorant of the Falkland

510

A trio of shags limber up their long, sinuous necks, much used in courtship. Moulting chinstrap penguin at right.

Islands, to thousands of pairs of guanays. The colonies are usually situated on rocky cliffs and the nests may be within a few feet of each other. Other colonies, especially those inland, may be in dead trees. The nest is a bowl of twigs, grasses, reeds or seaweed, which becomes plastered with the birds' droppings.

Courtship displays—the flightless cormorants' may take place in the water—involve much waving of the long neck. In soliciting, the female bends her neck right over her back.

The 2—4 eggs are incubated by both parents. The chicks hatch in 3—5 weeks. At first they are naked and have skins like black leather. Later they grow a curly, dark grey down. The parents feed them on fish, which the chicks take by pushing their heads down the parent's gullet. The chicks leave the nest in 5—8 weeks.

In peril at sea

The colonies are usually hard to get at, and by nesting on cliffs or in trees, cormorants are safe from enemies on land; but they sometimes get caught at sea. A humpback whale has been found dead with a cormorant stuck in its throat, having swallowed six others; and an angler fish that caught one was carried to the surface by the cormorant's buoyancy, but not in time to save the bird. Pike and cod have also been found with the remains of cormorants in their stomachs and leopard seals are known to chase them.

The blue-eyed shags of the sub-Antarctic seas face another problem. Dominican gulls have learned to wait by the flocks of feeding shags and steal the fish as the cormorants bring them to the surface. Sometimes the gulls dive in and intercept the shags as they are surfacing.

Cormorants keep their distance

Anyone who knows cormorants is familiar with the way they perch with wings held fully outspread. The generally accepted explanation is that the cormorant, that spends so much of its time in the water, is hanging out its wings to dry. It has been suggested that this is necessary because their wings are not very well waterproofed. Yet this would be most surprising in a family of birds who are not only aquatic themselves, but whose relatives such as pelicans, boobies and gannets are also aquatic. No other aquatic birds—except darters—hang their wings out to dry, and, furthermore, close observation does not suggest that standing with wings spread is connected with drying. Cormorants can be seen holding their wings open in pouring rain, when drying is im-

Cosmopolitan cormorants

Apart from the seas of the central Pacific, cormorants have a worldwide range stretching from Greenland to the sub-Antarctic islands. They will also frequent suitable stretches of water inland, the exception here being the northern Asian land mass.

Graham Pizzey: NHPA

John Tashjian at San Diego Zoo

possible, or after they have flown from one perch to another, when drying is not necessary. On other occasions they may come out of the sea and perch with wings folded'.

Cormorants habitually perch a short distance from each other, so a group of them on a rock are evenly spaced out in a line. When another bird lands, it extends its wings and its neighbours shift away. Then the newcomer folds its wings and the line of cormorants is still well-spaced with a wingspan between each one. So it seems that wing-spreading is a device that helps to keep individuals apart, for no animal likes being cheek by jowl with its neighbour. In sociable species, rituals are needed to promote harmony between individuals (see discussion on allopreening under avadavat, p 106) and courtship displays of birds reduce aggression and fear between the pair.

There may be another function. When they are frightened they suddenly fly off together, lumbering into the air with laboured wing beats. To make a clean getaway it is necessary to avoid collisions with neighbouring birds. Therefore, being spaced out is an advantage in a quick takeoff.

class	**Aves**
order	**Pelecaniformes**
family	**Phalacrocoracidae**
genera & species	***Phalacrocorax carbo*** *common cormorant* ***P. aristotelis*** *shag, others* ***Halietor pygmaeus*** *pigmy cormorant, others* ***Nannopterum harrisi*** *flightless cormorant*

512

Left: Pied cormorant and chick on the Abrolhos Islands, western Australia. Below: In captivity: flightless cormorant from the Galapagos Islands in the San Diego zoo. Although their wings are quite useless for flight, these cormorants adopt their flying relatives' typical 'wings-akimbo' stance. Right: Cormorant colonies usually nest on rocky cliffs within a few feet of each other, but some colonies — especially inland ones — will build nests in dead trees.

Atlas Vienne : Bavaria

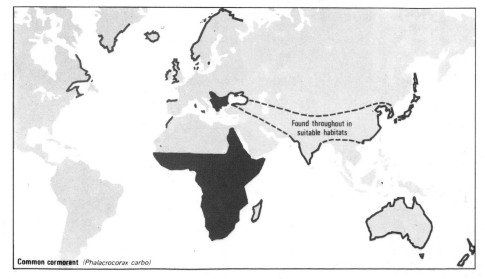

Found throughout in suitable habitats

Common cormorant (Phalacrocorax carbo)

Corncrake

Also called the land rail, the corncrake is a member of the rail family and is related to the coot and moorhen, which it resembles in form, although it is slightly smaller. It lives more on land than other rails. The plumage is yellowish-buff, marked with black on the upper parts, and greyish on head and breast. The wings are a rusty-red, very conspicuous when the bird is in flight.

Victims of progress

The corncrake breeds in Europe and Central Asia, from the south of Norway, Sweden and Finland to the Mediterranean coast, excluding Spain, Italy, Greece and the Balkans. During years of warm weather it extends its range northwards, but, overall, its range has decreased during this century. Originally agriculture helped the spread of the corncrake, for it is a bird of grassland, but now mechanical mowers have acted against it. At the turn of the century corncrakes were common over the British Isles. Now they are abundant only in the wilder parts of Western Ireland, the Hebrides, Orkney and Shetland, while a few breed regularly in some places on the mainland of Scotland and North Wales, all areas where there is little intensive agriculture.

Corncrakes are migratory, wintering in southern Asia and Africa, as far south as South Africa. Asian corncrakes reach Australia on very rare occasions. When flushed, corncrakes fly feebly, with legs dangling, so that it would seem strange that they can undertake long migrations. When on migration, however, the flight is steadier and more determined, but they fly near the ground and another possible cause of their decline is that they often run into overhead wires and cables.

Even where it is common, the corncrake is rarely seen because it is most active during the evening, when it skulks in the cover of vegetation, taking off only when alarmed. Nevertheless, its presence is well-advertised by the monotonous, two-beat call of the male which is kept up for hours on end both by day and night. The call is described as a creaking and can be imitated by running a piece of wood over the teeth of a comb.

Feeding

Corncrakes live on a variety of foods, mainly animal, and mostly insects such as beetles, earwigs, weevils and flies, including eggs and larvae as well as adults. Slugs and snails, earthworms, millipedes and spiders are eaten in smaller quantities. Plant food includes seeds, grains and some greenery.

Mother shoulders burden of family

The migrants reach the British Isles from their winter quarters in mid-April—mid-May. The males begin to call a few days after their arrival and continue for 2–3 weeks, stopping when the eggs are laid. They may start again after hatching and can be heard until late August, about a month before they migrate south again.

The male displays to the female with head held low, wings spread so the tips just touch the ground, and the feathers of the neck and sides fluffed out to form a ruff. He circles round her, moving his head from side to side and she turns all the time to keep facing him until mating.

The eggs, 6–14, are laid in a flat pad of plucked grass among grass, nettles, low undergrowth or in cereal crops. Low-lying water meadows seem to be preferred, but in upland areas corncrakes are found in pastures and crofts. The eggs are incubated by the female for 14–15 days. As she does

The wedge-shaped, elusive corncrake or land rail is on the decline in Britain. Once the spread of agriculture caused it to thrive, but now one of its most potent enemies is the combine harvester.

not start incubation until the last egg is laid, all hatch out within 24 hours. For about 4 days the chicks are fed by the female or by both parents. After that they can run about with the parents, feeding themselves. They start to fly when 5 weeks old, but cannot fly well for another 2 or 3 weeks.

Advancing agriculture defeats corncrakes

The downfall of the corncrake was brought about by the introduction of mowing machines and the progressive bringing forward of the hay-cutting season, so the date for haymaking coincided with the birds' nesting. This led to the destruction of eggs and young chicks. In Holland, at least, the corncrakes were able to avoid this to some extent by moving into cornfields, but this is only a temporary respite as there

is a similar trend for early harvesting of cereal crops.

In the British Isles, corncrakes began to decrease in the last quarter of the 19th century. They had never been common in many parts of East Anglia, but in 1875 it was noticed that fewer were nesting in Middlesex and the last record of nesting was in 1926. The decline spread northwards and westwards, although in the early parts of this century corncrakes could still be heard in Richmond Park, Kew Gardens, and on Wimbledon Common. The last strongholds in the British Isles began to fall after the Second World War, when mechanisation of agriculture reached the Scottish islands and the western side of Ireland. In the Shetland Islands the crofters used to leave the grass surrounding nests uncut; or if there were young these would be removed to the side of the field. Now mowing machines are used they still try to avoid the nests but these are usually too well camouflaged and cannot be seen in time. Their best chances of survival occur when the weather is bad and the harvest late.

class	**Aves**
order	**Gruiformes**
family	**Rallidae**
genus & species	*Crex crex*

Cotinga

Many of the cotingas have ornate plumage with brilliant colours, as well as crests, wattles and other adornments, while others such as the tityras and the becards are plainer. Only males are showy; the females are usually drab and inconspicuous. There are about 90 species in the family, which differ so widely in form that they were once placed in several families. The masked tityra is a 7in. long bird with black head and wings and grey body. The white-winged becard, although dull in colour, is still very pretty. The male is black on the upper parts with a grey rump and white wing patches. The female is olive-green above and pale yellow below. More ornate is the Pompadour cotinga with its lavender plumage and white wings. The female is grey. The Pompadour cotinga was named after Madame de Pompadour, by a British ornithologist, as the specimens he received were from a captured cargo ship on its way to France, where the cotinga feathers would have been used in the millinery made famous by the French courtesan.

The name cotinga comes from the Amazon Indian word for washed white and originally described the white bellbird, or snowy cotinga. A near relative is the three-wattled bellbird. This has reddish-brown plumage with a white head and chest and three whip-like wattles dangling from the base of the beak.

The two most ornate cotingas are the cock-of-the-rock (see p 472) and the umbrella bird which are treated under separate headings.

Cotingas are mainly birds of the dense forests in the Amazon basin, but they spread south to the northern borders of Argentina and north through Central America to the borders of the United States, living in pine and deciduous forests of high country and the bushy edges of forests as well as in the rain forests. One species, the Jamaican becard, has reached the West Indies, where it lives in the highlands of Jamaica.

Mystery voices

There are almost as many different ways of life as there are different body forms of the cotingas, living in the upper layers of foliage of dense forests. They are united in one family by their remarkable voices. It is for their persistent calling that they are best known. To the bird watcher fighting his way through the undergrowth the calls may be the only sign of cotingas which are flitting about in the dense greenery high overhead. The bellbirds, for instance, like the other birds in Australia and New Zealand that have the same name, produce loud, bell-like peals that can be heard a mile or so away. The calf or capuchin bird, chestnut brown with black tail and wings and a bare blue-grey patch of skin on its face, makes a mooing or grunting call. The

Naked-throated bellbird

E Lindsey

△ *The three-wattled bellbird sports three slim wattles sprouting from the base of its bill.*

△ *Rieffer's cotinga. The cotinga family is mostly confined to the tropical forests of central and South America, but some species have spread to the southern borders of the USA and to the Caribbean.*

tityras also 'grunt' in a most unbirdlike manner. Other cotingas are less vocal, some having very quiet songs. The white-winged becard, however, is a notable songster, singing from March to September. It has a special dawn song that can be heard, almost without a break, for an hour after sunrise.

Feeding

Many cotingas are fruit eaters, but some eat a proportion of insects. The tityras which have hooked, shrike-like bills will catch dragonflies and lizards, and the white-winged becards have been seen flying up to foliage and picking insects off without landing.

Elaborate courtship and hidden nests

In keeping with their brilliant plumage, the male cotingas often have elaborate courtship rituals. After courtship and mating the females rear the families on their own. The climax of courtship displays in the cotingas is reached by the cock-of-the-rock (see p 472) when several males gather in one place to display. Other cotingas have special grounds but they display alone. The bearded bellbird courts and mates on a special branch, as does the capuchin bird which clears its branch of twigs by neatly snapping them off with its bill.

The less brilliant cotingas have a more formal married life. The tityras remain paired the whole year round and although the male does not help with nest-building or the incubation of the two eggs he will fly about with the female, keeping her company. Similarly, the male white-winged becard sings to his mate while she builds the nest. This is a bulky construction, built high in the treetops with a doorway in the side. The 3 or 4 eggs are incubated for 18–19 days, and the male helps to feed the fledglings which stay in the nest for 21 days.

The masked tityra makes her nest in a hole, usually one abandoned by a woodpecker, as much as 100 ft up. The nest is made by dropping dead leaves and twiglets, plucked from nearby branches, into the cavity. More material may be added during incubation. As tityra nests are usually high in trees that are often very rotten, few observations have been made on them and the incubation period is unknown. Alexander Skutch, a well-known American ornithologist, once managed to climb up to the nest of a masked tityra but he said that he did so only when enthusiasm overruled judgement and that he did not advise it as a pastime. In this case the tree stood in deep water behind a dam and was consequently very rotten, but Dr Skutch decided it was worth the attempt because if something snapped and he fell, landing in water was better than landing on land. With the aid of a ladder and the encouragement of his companion he reached the nest to find a hollow, 1 ft deep, with an inch layer of leaf fragments on which two coffee-coloured eggs lay.

Enemies take over their nests

Cotinga nests may be destroyed by the nest-robbing toucans called araçaris, but sometimes tityras have been found successfully rearing broods in the same trees that the araçaris were using. Parasitic flycatchers have been known to destroy becard nests and to rear their own families in them, and a species of large black bee will do likewise, blocking up the nest entrance with wax.

Crowding the neighbours

Not all birds that live in holes are able to excavate their own. Like some mammals that live in others' burrows, they nest in cavities abandoned by woodpeckers and others. The tityras go even further: they oust the rightful owners by haunting the nest-hole and making a nuisance of themselves until the owners are forced to move. This is because the tityras, although normally mild-mannered, refuse to relinquish a hole once they have set their hearts on it. At first they probably claim it, in all innocence, while the owner is away. They then start to bring nesting material and drop it into the cavity. At first there is retaliation, and the woodpeckers or toucans that first had the hole remove the leaf litter that the tityras bring in. The tityras, however, appear to win through sheer persistence. While the other birds are away during the day the tityras can accumulate a good pile of leaves. Dr Skutch relates how three araçaris that shared a hole for roosting had difficulty squeezing into it, because of the material brought in by a pair of tityras. They had to abandon the normal method of entering headfirst and turn around for the more awkward method of backing in with tail doubled over. Sometimes they could not all get in and one or two had to sleep elsewhere. The tityras were now firmly convinced to whom the hole belonged and attacked the much larger araçaris as they tried to get in, and, luckily for them, the latter eventually gave up and moved to a hole that did not shrink every day.

class	**Aves**
order	**Passeriformes**
family	**Cotingidae**
genera & species	***Procnias averano*** *bearded bellbird* **P. tricarunculata** *three-wattled bellbird* **Tityra semifasciata** *masked tityra* **Xipholena punicea** *Pompadour cotinga others*

Caught by the camera: a cottontail surprised while resting prepares to make itself scarce. These rabbits fall prey to every flesh-eater in their region, and often need all their flashing speed to escape.

Cottontail

The cottontail is a small rabbit varying from dark grey to reddish-brown. The upper parts are brown and sides grey, with a rufous nape and legs. The ears are short and rounded. The tail is brown above and white below and gives rise to the name cottontail from its resemblance to a cotton boll. There are about 13 species whose head and body length varies from 10–18 in. and weight from 14 oz–5 lb.

Abundant everywhere

Cottontail rabbits of various kinds range from southern Canada to South America, as far as Argentina and Paraguay. Over this range they live in a wide variety of habitats. Most species prefer open woodland and brush or clearings in forests. Consequently some species flourished in early colonial times when European settlers were first opening up the forests. Later, complete destruction of forests acted ·against these species. The New England cottontail of the Appalachians preferred open woodland with undergrowth, but with the spread of agriculture this species has been replaced by the Eastern cottontail that inhabits open country such as pastureland.

Other species of cottontail live in more extreme habitats. The smallest species, the Idaho cottontail, lives in deserts, and the largest, the swamp or marsh rabbit, sometimes called the 'canecutter', lives in swampy areas. It has large feet with splayed, slightly furred toes, and swims well. When alarmed it is said to make for water where it hides with only nose and ears showing.

Cottontails are timid animals, ready to bolt for cover at the slightest hint of danger, finding a suitable place where they crouch motionless, their neutral colour blending in so well with the vegetation that they are very difficult to find. In this they are aided by their nocturnal habits. Most species are active when the light is dim, but during the summer months, when nights are short, the cottontails are more active and are more likely to be seen in broad daylight.

Each cottontail has a range of several acres that is crossed by regular runs through the ground vegetation. In these runs the animal knows its way so well that it can hurtle at a full speed of 20–25 mph when frightened. Cottontails usually use the burrows of other animals, such as woodchucks. Only the Idaho cottontail makes its own burrow.

Making the most of their food

Cottontails eat grass and broad-leaved annuals and can severely damage crops and gardens. The damage is made the more severe because more plants are injured than eaten. Some are trampled and others only nibbled, sufficient to spoil them as a food crop without satisfying the cottontail's hunger. If this is done to young plants they grow stunted and deformed. In winter the cottontails feed on buds and soft twigs, and young saplings can be found neatly cut off at the level of the snowline.

Digestion of coarse herbage and twigs is difficult, as they contain large quantities of indigestible cellulose, which has to be assimilated. Other grazing animals, such as cows and sheep, chew the cud, a process in which food first goes to the rumen, the first compartment of the multiple stomach, where the cellulose is broken down, then brought up to the mouth and back to the true stomach. In rabbits another process is used. Food is passed through the digestive system twice, to ensure complete digestion, by eating the faeces containing food undigested after the first time through.

Breeding like other rabbits

The breeding season is long, from February to September in temperate parts of North America, but in arid areas such as the Sierra Nevada it starts earlier, for in summer the vegetation will have shrivelled and there will be little food for the young. In some parts where conditions are always favourable, breeding may take place all the year round.

Fighting sometimes occurs between males, with fur flying, and courtship dances may take place in which one rabbit leaps in the air while the other runs under it. After mating the male is driven away and the female rears the litter alone. The young cottontails, called fawns, are born a month after mating, naked and blind. There may be up to seven of them, weighing less than 1 oz each. They are placed in a shallow nest that the mother has scraped in the ground, perhaps by enlarging the hoofprint of a horse or cow, and lined with grass and fur plucked from her breast. When she leaves the nest she carefully covers it with grass. The nest is so small that the mother cannot lie in it. Instead she crouches over it and the fawns have to climb up to suckle.

When a fortnight old the fawns leave the nest and feed nearby during the day. They finally disperse when 3 weeks old. Their mother will have mated again within a few hours of their birth and the next litter will soon be due. She may have up to 5 litters in a year.

Every man's meat

Cottontails fall prey to every flesh-eating animal. Skunks, foxes and crows search out and kill the young in the nests and owls, hawks, snakes and chickarees take the young when they leave their nests. Other predators such as bobcats and eagles take the adults. Man also hunts and traps cottontails and in the eastern United States

517

they are the chief game animal, sometimes several million cottontails being killed annually in one State. Their fur is of little use except in the manufacture of felt, but they are eaten, although care is needed in handling and cooking them as a rabbit disease called turalemia is infectious to man. Proper cooking is sufficient to kill all germs.

Ample food for all

The cottontail, whose only defence is not to be seen as it crouches motionless, half hidden by greenery, forms the staple food of many American predators, much in the same way as the European rabbit once was the mainstay of many carnivores and birds of prey on the other side of the Atlantic. The importance of the cottontail in the natural economy has been shown in studies of the feeding habits of the predators.

One method of finding out an animal's food preferences is to examine the undigested remains passed out in the excrement. Bones of small mammals and birds are often easily identifiable, and while fishbones are usually digested, their earbones, or otoliths, may pass through unchanged. The shells of snails and other molluscs may also be present, along with feathers and fur. This method has to be used carefully because it can give misleading results. For instance, fish remains are rarely found around herons' nests because the bones are so easily digested.

In a study made in the Sierra Nevada, cottontails were found to be the staple diet of coyotes, grey foxes, bobcats, horned owls and gopher snakes. The horned owl's diet consisted of 61% cottontails. Rattlesnakes and red-tailed hawks also took large numbers of cottontails, but preferred ground squirrels. These predators are only the main natural enemies of cottontails in this region, and, as well as other animals which take cottontails only occasionally, we must add man, floods and disease as agents that significantly reduce their numbers.

The point of cataloguing the sources of dangers to cottontails is to demonstrate the vast numbers of cottontails that must exist. In the study of the predators' feeding preferences it was calculated that they captured over 7 lb of cottontails each year on every acre of ground. So more than the actual cottontail population is being eaten by only some of their enemies, but the apparent contradiction is solved by the extremely rapid rate of breeding. Each female cottontail is producing litters, averaging four young, 3—5 times a year. If those struck down by a predator only weigh 1 lb, there is still a good surplus left to continue the species.

The cottontail's watchword: run for your life

Photos by L Lee Rue III: Photo Res.

class	**Mammalia**
order	**Lagomorpha**
family	**Leporidae**
genus	*Sylvilagus*

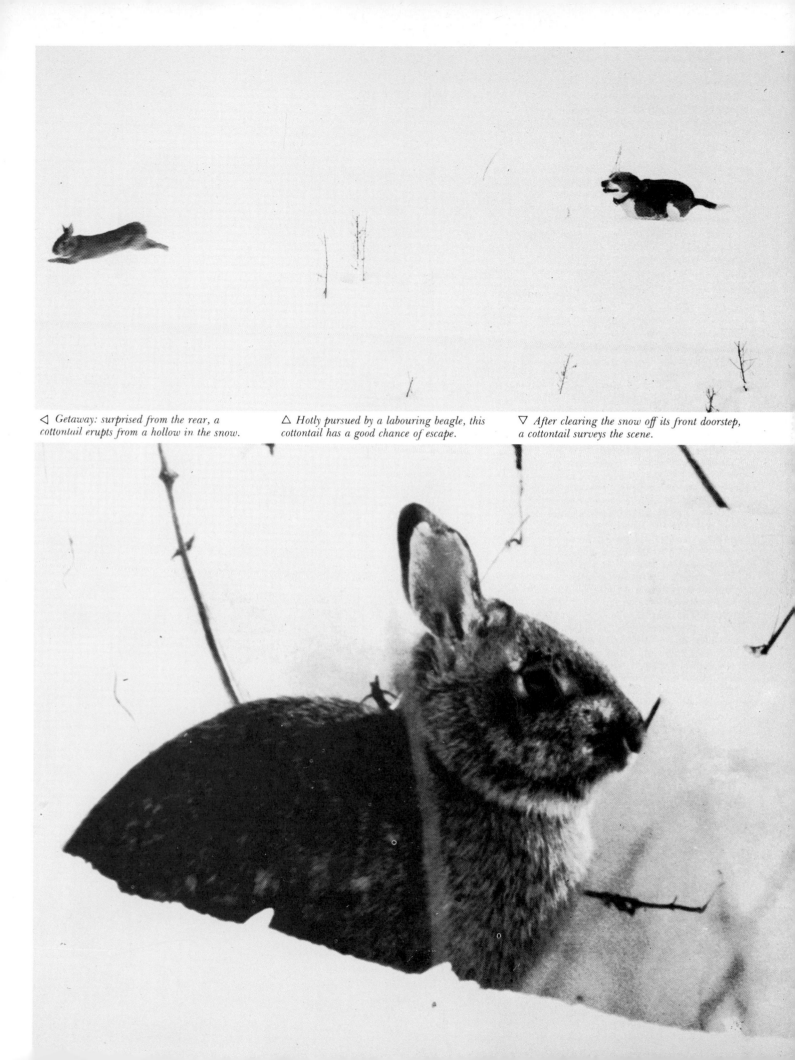

◁ *Getaway: surprised from the rear, a cottontail erupts from a hollow in the snow.*

△ *Hotly pursued by a labouring beagle, this cottontail has a good chance of escape.*

▽ *After clearing the snow off its front doorstep, a cottontail surveys the scene.*

Coucal

Despite being members of the cuckoo family, coucals do not lay their eggs in other birds' nests, but make their own. There are about 27 species which are large by cuckoo standards. The pheasant coucal or swamp cuckoo of Australia is 23 in. long with the long tail, characteristic of the cuckoo family, exaggerated to give it a pheasant-like appearance. The tail and rump are a glossy greenish-black, barred with brown and white, while the rest of the plumage is brown or buff with black bars. In the breeding season the male's plumage becomes glossy green-black on the head, neck and underparts.

According to some authorities, the couas of Madagascar belong to the same subfamily as the coucals. They are very similar to the coucals both in form and habit, but there are only about 10 species, compared with the coucal's 27.

Wary bush fowls

Coucals are found in Africa, from Somalia and Senegal to the Cape, as well as in Asia and Australia, reaching as far east as the Solomon Islands. Although widespread and not uncommon in some places, they are not very well known because of their shy habits. Many coucals, including the pheasant coucal and the black coucal, live in swampy country. They prefer to lurk in thick cover, flying as little as possible. The black coucal of central Africa is very difficult to flush once disturbed, and the Senegal coucal hops from bough to bough through bushes, flapping clumsily across open spaces. The blue-headed coucal, however, can often be seen in the morning and evening when it sits on tops of reeds and high grass.

Being so secretive in their habits, coucals are best known by their calls. Many have bubbling calls sounding like water being poured from a bottle. Others have a whooping call, from which the name coucal is derived. The blue-headed coucal has a low 'cou-cou-cou' which is immediately answered by its mate, the call and answer being used to keep in touch while moving about in thick undergrowth. The white-browed coucal also 'bubbles', a pair singing duets in which one bird sings at a higher pitch. It also has a harsh 'chak' call. This is heard especially during and after rain, and as a result this bird has become known as the rainbird in parts of Africa.

Diet of small animals

The blue-headed coucal has the most liberal diet. It feeds on insects, hunts small birds, lizards and reptiles and is also a scavenger. The white-browed coucal that sometimes lives in gardens or fields takes large numbers of grasshoppers and snails as well as snakes and other vertebrates. The pheasant coucal robs nests and occasionally takes to raiding chicken runs. It also kills mice and other small mammals.

▷ *A pheasant coucal feeds its chicks. In this species the cuckoo-like long tail is exaggerated.*

African relative: the Senegal coucal. The coucals tend to build well-camouflaged nests near the ground, in low bushes or grass clumps. Poor fliers, they spend much of their time on the ground.

Peter Johnson

Well hidden nests

Nests are well camouflaged and built near the ground, in a low bush or tussock of grass. The pheasant coucal's nest is built in a large tussock by drawing the tops of the grass stems together to make a hollow of 4in. diameter, lined with green leaves. It has an opening at either end and the coucal sits on the eggs with head and long tail protruding. Sometimes these nests have an entrance tunnel, also lined with green leaves, which are replaced as they dry out and turn brown. Pheasant coucals have been known, although rarely, to make their nests in deserted babblers' nests.

Both sexes incubate 3–5 eggs for a fortnight. The chicks take about 20 days to fledge. The white-browed coucal is reported to carry its young, one at a time, between its thighs when danger threatens, as from a forest fire. Woodcocks are well known for this behaviour and it is likely

that when all the coucals have been better studied it will be found that other species do the same.

An uneatable pheasant

The common coucal of southeast Asia is known in Malaya and India as the large crow pheasant. As with the pheasant coucal of Australia, the name refers to its long pheasant-like tail feathers. In Malaya the coucal's large size and chestnut and black plumage make it look even more like a pheasant as it runs through the undergrowth or flies heavily across open spaces. As a result inexperienced hunters are likely to shoot in error. An even worse mistake is made if the proud hunter carries it home and persuades his wife that it would make a welcome addition to the menu. Coucal does not resemble pheasant in taste. It is quite uneatable. Even the forest

dwelling aborigines of Malaya, who will eat practically anything else, balk at eating coucal.

It would be interesting to know whether other flesh-eating animals find coucals distasteful. If they did, it would be of great value as a protection from enemies. One meal convinces any human hunter of the futility of hunting coucals; and so, for the sacrifice of a few coucals, the remainder would be safe from non-human enemies who had learned their error.

class	**Aves**
order	**Cuculiformes**
family	**Cuculidae**
genus & species	***Centropus phasianus*** *pheasant coucal* ***C. superciliosus*** *white-browed coucal* ***C. sinensis*** *crow pheasant, others*

521

Courser

Together with the pratincoles, the nine coursers form a family of long-legged, plover-like shorebirds. The most familiar to ornithologists is the cream-coloured courser, a starling-sized bird. It is a pale sandy colour, with creamy legs, distinctive black primary wing feathers and a broad, black and white eye stripe. Temminck's, Burchell's and the Indian coursers are rather similar, but the plumage is much darker. The Australian courser is known to the Australians, incorrectly, as a dotterel. The Egyptian plover, also misnamed, is different from the others. It is a beautiful grey and white with black and green markings.

Coursers live in the Old World from Africa to Australia, six of the nine species breeding in Africa. The cream-coloured courser breeds from the Cape Verde Islands to Persia and south to Kenya. It is a familiar bird of the fringes of the Sahara and occasionally wanders north into Europe. It has occasionally been seen in the British Isles. Of the two Indian species Jerdon's courser is probably extinct. The last record was in 1900.

Desert runners

As their name suggests, coursers are good runners and, like many birds that have specialised in running, they have lost the fourth, backward-facing toe. Although they can fly well, some migrating considerable distances, they can usually only be forced to take off if chased very hard.

Coursers generally live in dry sandy places or in grassland, the exception being the Egyptian plover which lives along sandy river banks, and Temminck's courser which lives in woods and forests where there are open spaces.

Outside the breeding season coursers gather in small parties. As they run about, they have the habit of stopping to stretch up on tiptoe and crane their necks to peer around them. When frightened they crouch down to conceal themselves against the ground, rather than take flight.

Feeding

Coursers live mainly on insects such as beetles, grasshoppers, ants, flies and caterpillars, but they also eat snails and occasionally small lizards.

Eggs are watered to keep cool

As a rule, coursers do not make a nest, laying their two or three eggs on the bare ground, but Temminck's courser and the Australian dotterel sometimes make a depression in the ground. The eggs are incubated, or shielded from the sun, by the female alone. The Egyptian plover broods its eggs during the night when the air and soil surface cool down rapidly, while in the daytime it covers the eggs with sand to prevent them from getting too hot.

Neither the length of the incubation period nor the time the young spend with their parents are known. They can run very

Peter Johnson

△ *Stolid parent: a courser squats on its eggs. Coursers do not usually build nests, but lay their eggs on the bare ground; although sometimes they will make a small hollow to lay in.*

▽ *A black-backed courser cleans its bill. Long-legged, plover-like shorebirds, coursers are good runners, and have lost the normal backward-facing toe in their evolution.*

Constance P Warner

shortly after hatching, but are shaded from the sun by each parent in turn during the middle of the day. The Egyptian plover also buries its chicks, partially or completely, as with the eggs. Chicks have been found an inch or more under the surface, which is sufficient to protect them from the worst of the heat, while not being too deep to prevent them from breathing. Furthermore, the parents cool the sand by fetching water from a nearby river and regurgitating it over the place where the chicks are buried.

Another habit of the Egyptian plover, and of the Australian dotterel, and, for all we know, of other coursers, is to hastily bury their chicks if danger threatens. The chicks flatten themselves against the ground, if possible in a small depression. Hippopotamus footprints have been described as being a suitable hiding place. The adult then hastily kicks sand over the crouching chicks and makes its own escape, running away and luring the enemy from the chicks.

The crocodile's toothpick

If the Egyptian plover's parental behaviour is not sufficient to brand it as a bird with unusual habits the story of the crocodile bird, dating from the Greeks, will confirm it.

The crocodile bird, or trochilus as it was then called, was supposed to enter a crocodile's mouth as it lay basking with its mouth open to pick pieces of meat from between its teeth and leeches from its gums. The Elizabethan writers, notably John Leo, told how the trochilus avoided being eaten by pricking the roof of the crocodile's mouth with a special spike on its head if the latter attempted to close its mouth. In another version, however, the crocodile was not so discourteous and moved its head as a signal that it intended to close its mouth.

As with many of the old animal stories, the reaction of modern scientists has been to pour scorn, then, somewhat begrudgingly, accept at least a basis of truth in them. Modern writers disagree as to the validity of the crocodile bird story but some report seeing birds that pick parasites off the crocodile's skin, entering their mouths as well. Sandpipers and Egyptian plovers have been seen taking leeches from the tongue.

These birds, apparently in great danger when performing these operations, are probably quite safe because animals such as crocodiles have very fixed patterns of behaviour. While basking, they are not interested in hunting, so even food in the mouth does not arouse them. This is also the explanation for small birds being able to nest within the nests of eagles with complete safety. That is, so long as the bird is on its nest its hunting instincts are inhibited.

class	**Aves**
order	**Charadriiformes**
family	**Glareolidae**
genera & species	**Cursor cursor** *cream-coloured courser*
	C. temminckii *Temminck's courser*
	C. coromandelicus *Indian courser*
	Peltohyas australis *Australian dotterel*
	Pluvianus aegyptus *Egyptian plover*
	others

Arthur Christiansen

△ *The double-banded courser, unlike its relatives, only lays one egg. Observers once saw a double-banded courser lay its egg at the height of the dry season in northern Tanzania—and both parents then took turns at standing over the egg (and later the chick) to keep it shadowed from the blazing sun. Other species will kick sand over their chicks to conceal them, and lure potential enemies away.*

Courser (family Glareolidae)

◁ *Ranging from Africa to Australia, there are 9 species of courser—and 6 of them breed in Africa. The cream-coloured courser occasionally wanders north into Europe, and has sometimes been seen in Britain. Two species are reported in India, of which one —Jerdon's courser— is now probably extinct.*

Constance P Warner

△ *Restricted species: the baywinged cowbird, found in Argentina, Bolivia, Paraguay, Uruguay, and the coasts of Brazil.*

▷ *Widespread species: the glossy or shiny cowbird, ranging south from Venezuela as far as the central regions of Argentina.*

Cowbird

The three genera of cowbirds are related to grackles, troupials, and others. They are smallish birds, with glossy dark plumage. The shiny cowbird is 7 in. long with a conical, finch-like bill, and a glossy greenish-black and violet plumage. The screaming cowbird has a dull glossy plumage of blue-black with some green in the wings and tail. The common brown-headed cowbird of America, apart from the brown head, is greenish-black.

An American habitat
The various species of cowbirds are confined to America, most of them being found in the southern half of the continent. Some are fairly restricted. The baywinged cowbird, for example, is found in Argentina, Bolivia, Paraguay and Uruguay, and on the coasts of Brazil. The shiny cowbird, on the other hand, is widespread in South America from Venezuela and Colombia to the mid-region of Argentina. The brown-headed cowbird ranges across North America from the Pacific to Atlantic coasts. Its northern boundary runs from Nova Scotia, along the northern shores of the Great Lakes, up to the Great Slave Lake and down to Vancouver, and it ranges south to the borders of Mexico and Yucatan.

Cowbirds and cuckoos
Cowbirds could be called the cuckoos of the Americas because of the way they breed, although their common name is derived from their habit of following cattle to feed. They live in open country, spending the winter months in flocks and splitting into pairs that hold territories during the breeding season. Some species are sedentary; others, such as the shiny cowbird and brown-headed cowbird, migrate in spring and autumn.

A menace to growing crops
Cowbirds eat seeds and insects, the latter mostly during the summer when they are abundant. Many kinds of seeds are eaten and some cowbirds will feed on spilt grain around farmyards. In some places they are a considerable menace when they attack growing crops. This is especially so in the late summer when breeding is over. They descend on the ripening rice or corn fields in large flocks that are so dense that farmers kill 70 or 80 at a time with a double-barrelled shotgun blast.

At other times the cowbirds are beneficial, following the plough in search of grubs. This habit may be a development of their more usual one, of following cattle or other livestock to feed on the insects flushed from the grass by the large animals' hoofs. This is the reason for their name, and in some parts of North America they are called buffalo birds because before the buffalo (American bison) were killed off the cowbirds associated with them, walking behind the buffalo as they grazed or perching on their backs. An Indian legend describes cowbirds nesting in the wool between a buffalo's horns, and Ernest Thompson Seton tells of a cowbird that did not migrate one winter. Instead it made a nest in the wool on a buffalo's back in which to sleep.

The cuckoo's nesting habit
The parasitic habit of laying eggs in another bird's nest is not confined to the cuckoo. Several kinds of birds do this, including the cowbirds. Over 250 different species are parasitised by the brown-headed cowbird, although some are preferred to others. Most of its eggs are laid in the nests of its relatives, the orioles, but one study showed that up to 80% of song sparrow nests are victimised by various kinds of cowbirds. The female cowbird lays her eggs in the nest at the same time as the owner is laying hers, and before she has started to incubate them. By keeping a close watch, the cowbird notes when the other bird leaves her nest, then she sneaks in and lays an egg in under a minute. Unlike the cuckoos, the baby cowbirds do not throw the other eggs out of the nest, but the adult cowbird will come back after laying her own egg and remove one or more in her bill.

Each cowbird lays four or five eggs, usually one in each of several nests, but if there is a shortage of nests several cowbirds will lay in one nest. As many as 37 shiny cowbird eggs have been found in the nest of one ovenbird.

Some birds reject the cowbird's eggs. Tyrant flycatchers build a new floor to the nest, covering the trespassing eggs. Others, such as catbirds and American robins, throw the eggs out, and some birds desert their nests altogether if they are parasitized. If, however, the cowbird egg is accepted it stands a very good chance of survival. Cowbird eggs hatch in a shorter time than the eggs of their host birds, so they have a good start in the competition for food that there always is between nestlings. Sometimes, this results in the death of the other nestlings, but not invariably so and two or three other nestlings, as well as the cowbird, may be reared. The young cowbird grows rapidly and leaves the nest in under two weeks, but it is still fed for another week.

Parental laziness

Not all cowbirds are parasites. The baywinged cowbird of South America rears its own offspring, both parents helping to feed the young. But even so there are some signs of the parental laziness of the true parasite. Very often the baywinged cowbird builds its own nest out of grass and feathers and most of the work is done by the male. However, if there are any abandoned nests of other species available, the cowbirds take them over, perhaps adding a few pieces of their own material. The next stage is represented by the screaming cowbird which ousts the rightful owner, who, surprisingly, is always the baywinged cowbird, while it is still in possession. From here one can see that a bird could merely take to laying its eggs in a nest rather than permanently displacing the owners. The shiny cowbird does this, and it has not completely lost the habit of nest building. During courtship it gathers nesting material and half-heartedly attempts to build a nest. At the end of this scale of increasing dependence on other birds is the brown-headed cowbird which no longer has any home of its own. It leaves its children on other people's doorsteps.

class	**Aves**
order	**Passeriformes**
family	**Icteridae**
genera & species	***Molothrus badius*** *baywinged cowbird*
	M. rufo-axillaris *screaming cowbird*
	M. bonariensis *shiny cowbird*
	M. ater *brown-headed cowbird*
	Tangavius armenti *Arment's cowbird*

Coyote

The coyote belongs with domestic dogs and wolves in the genus **Canis.** *The name comes from the Mexican* **coyotl** *and can be pronounced with or without the 'e' silent. A coyote weighs 20—50 lb and measures about 4 ft from nose to tail-tip. The fur is tawny and the tail, bushy with a black tip, droops low behind the hind legs, instead of being carried horizontally as wolves do. Another difference from wolves is that coyotes are smaller, and they hunt smaller game than wolves.*

Coyotes used to live on plains and in woods of the western part of North America, being known as the brush wolf in forested regions and the prairie wolf in open lands. Within the last century their range has increased despite persecution and they are now found from north Alaska to Costa Rica. They have also spread eastwards to the Atlantic seaboard. At the turn of the century they had reached Michigan; they were seen in New York State in 1925 and in Massachusetts in 1957. The northward spread carried them to the southern shores of Hudson's Bay by 1961.

The prairie wolf's spread

In the face of man's persecution most carnivorous animals have been retreating. Their habitat has been destroyed and they are hunted mercilessly as vermin or as valuable fur bearers. The coyote is extending its range. There is no market for its fur but the coyote has long been shot on sight, or trapped and poisoned, because it has been regarded as an enemy of livestock and a competitor against man for game. Many thousands have been killed—125 000 a year according to one estimate—yet the coyotes flourish. Their powers of survival seem to lie in their proverbial wariness and their adaptability. They are difficult to trap unless a ruse is employed. One coyote avoided every trap set for it until the trapper buried an alarm clock near a trap and the coyote, overcome by curiosity, walked right into it.

The spread into the northeast United States is probably linked with widespread tree-felling and the decline and extinction of the timber wolf. This left a gap in the wildlife of the area which the adaptable coyote was able to fill. Even urban development has not deterred coyotes. They have moved into suburbs where, like the red fox in Britain, they can supplement their diet with gleanings from dustbins and other sources. There is a story of a Californian who wondered why his dog was not gaining weight despite being very well fed. He later discovered that a pair of coyotes were stealing its food. One lured the dog away while the other bolted the contents of the feeding bowl.

Give a dog a bad name . . .

Coyotes are persecuted because of their reputation as killers of livestock and deer. While sheep, goats and deer are occasionally killed, the reputation has probably been encouraged by the coyote's carrion-eating habits. A half-eaten carcase of a cow or sheep with coyote tracks around it leads to the assumption that coyotes killed it, and revenge is extracted without thought that the animal might have died for some other reason, such as thirst.

As proof that coyotes are not major threats to livestock, several thousand dead coyotes have been examined. Their stomachs contained mainly jack rabbits and cottontails, together with mice, voles and other small rodents. Poultry and livestock made up about $\frac{1}{8}$ of the sample. It is probable that, as with other animals with a varied diet, coyotes will eat whatever is most available. If rabbits are abundant, then poultry runs are left alone, but if a square meal in the form of a weak calf is found,

then it is not overlooked. Many other items are eaten; insects, birds, trout and crayfish have been found in coyote stomachs. Beavers, domestic cats, skunks and even grey foxes have been known to be attacked and eaten. Sometimes coyotes eat large amounts of vegetable matter, including prickly pears, grass and nuts. They are said to be very fond of water melons, taking only the ripe ones.

Coyotes hunt singly or in pairs, running down their prey with speeds of over 40 mph. Sometimes they chase deer in relays, one coyote taking over the pursuit as another becomes tired. Another habit is to sham dead, waiting for inquisitive, carrion-eating birds such as crows to land and examine the 'corpse', when it leaps up and grabs them.

Coyotes are model parents

Breeding begins when coyotes are a year old and they pair for life. They mate during January to March and the pups are born 63 days later. The den is usually made in a burrow abandoned by a woodchuck, skunk or fox, which is enlarged to form a tunnel up to 30 ft long and 1–2 ft in diameter, ending in a nesting chamber which is kept scrupulously clean. Nests are sometimes made on the surface—for instance, in marshlands where tunnels would be flooded.

Up to 19 pups may be born in a litter, the average being around 10. They are born with their eyes shut and stay underground for over a month. The father stays with the family, bringing food first for the mother, then for the pups; this is regurgitated to them as a partly-digested mess. Later the family go out on communal hunting trips and the pups learn to hunt for themselves. Although hunters themselves, coyotes are not immune to being attacked by larger predators, and coyotes are known to have been killed by wolves, golden eagles and pumas.

The call of the West

Scientifically the coyote is *Canis latrans,* barking dog, so-called because apart from the domestic dog it is the only member of the dog family that habitually barks. Foxes, wolves and jackals only bark at specific times. The call of the coyote has become part of the background to the Wild West, necessary to produce 'atmosphere' for any night scene in a Western film. Coyotes can be heard all the year round, usually at dawn and dusk. In the evening coyotes sing in chorus. One starts with a series of short barks, gradually increasing in volume until they merge into a long yell. Other coyotes join in and the chorus continues for a minute or two. After a pause, the chorus starts again.

Two or three coyotes may meet each night to sing and the eerie effect of the songs of several such groups ringing over the countryside on a still moonlight night is very impressive. Not surprisingly, there are numerous legends connected with the coyotes' song. The faraway sound is supposed to be made by the coyote barking into a badger hole to produce a hollow echo, while the quavering howl is said to be produced by the coyote making its chest vibrate by bouncing on rigid legs.

Many Indians claimed to understand the coyotes' language. The Comanches had their equivalent to Kipling's Mowgli, who was brought up by coyotes and later taught his tribe to understand them.

class	**Mammalia**
order	**Carnivora**
family	**Canidae**
genus & species	***Canis latrans***

Winter feast: coyotes clean an elk carcase while ravens wait for their turn.

△ *Coyote pups. Up to 19 may be born in one litter, but the average is 10. After a month underground, the pups begin to sally out on communal hunting trips until they learn to fend for themselves.*

▽ *Suspicion: a swimming coyote approaches the bank. Hunters themselves, coyotes are known to have been attacked by larger predators.*

Coyote:
the fast-loping
prairie wolf

▷ *A coyote heads in to intercept a deer. When it comes to a straight chase, coyotes often find themselves outpaced by deer, and have been known to wear down their quarry by chasing in relays until it tires.*

▽ *A coyote in its classic pose as the spirit of the North American prairie — but within the last century they have spread across North America from Alaska to Costa Rica.*

▽▷ *A young coyote emerges from its lair. Coyotes live in scrupulously clean nesting chambers at the end of tunnels which can be up to 30 ft long.*

Joe Van Wormer: Photo Res.

Joe Van Wormer: Photo Res.

Crabeater seal

Of the five true seals living around the coasts of the Antarctic, the crabeater is the smallest. It is a slender, lithe animal with a small head, measuring at most 8—9 ft from snout to tail and weighing up to 500 lb. The females are usually slightly larger than the males.

The name white seal has been given to crabeaters on account of their creamy white fur, which is moulted in January (mid-summer in the southern hemisphere) to a greyish brown. During the year this fades back to white.

Life in the pack ice

Crabeaters are the most numerous seals in the Antarctic, if not in the world. Estimates of their numbers range from 2—5 million, accurate estimation being difficult because they live in the pack ice where man can reach them only by icebreaker or aeroplane. Counts of seals are regularly made from ships threading their way through the ice fields, and crabeaters are noticeably more common than other seals, but the number of seals seen basking on the ice floes is not a true indication of their real numbers. It is impossible to know how many other seals are in the water. This number depends, at least in part, on the weather, for seals prefer to come out in calm, sunny conditions.

In summer the crabeaters move south as the pack ice breaks up, and they are found closer to the shore. When more detailed studies can be made it may be found that they have proper migrations from north to south. Some individuals wander north, reaching Australia, New Zealand and Uruguay.

Crabeaters can move over the ice at surprising speed. They throw themselves forwards by pushing at the packed snow and ice with hind and front flippers in a sort of undulating, caterpillar-like action. Speeds of 15 mph have been recorded.

They eat krill, not crab

Most seals feed on fish, and crabeaters are no exception, but their main food is the shrimp-like crustacean called krill, the same animal that forms the staple diet of penguins, whales and many Antarctic sea birds. So 'krilleater' would be a better name. To catch krill in sufficient numbers to be efficient, crabeaters have a device to strain them from the water very much like the baleen plates that the blue whale, for instance, uses to strain krill (see p 248). In crabeater seals the teeth act as a strainer. Each tooth has five cusps, like battlements on a castle. The seal sucks in a mouthful of krill and water, then shuts its mouth so the teeth on upper and lower jaws fit closely together. It then forces water out through the gaps between the cusps, leaving the krill behind. The straining system is completed by bony growths at the back of the jaws that fill the gap behind the teeth that is present in other mammals. (This gap can be felt by feeling behind one's rear teeth with the tongue while the mouth is shut.)

The peculiar shape of the crabeater's teeth is probably derived from the sharp, cusped teeth of other seals, like the leopard seal, which are used to grip the slippery bodies of fish and squid.

Breeding at sea

Because crabeaters bear their pups in the remote fastnesses of the pack ice, little is known about their breeding habits. Females are thought to mate first when 2 years old,

A group of crabeaters lounges on an Antarctic floe. They are the most numerous seals in the Antarctic, if not the whole world.

bearing their single pups a year later, in October. Although crabeaters often gather on the ice in large numbers, pupping takes place in small groups. They prefer ice where the floes are not too closely packed together, but have been thrown into hummocks which provide shelter from the wind.

The newborn pups are about 4 ft long, 55 lb in weight and are covered in a soft, woolly coat. Information differs as to whether the pups are suckled for 2 or 4 weeks. The baby coat is presumably shed when the pup is weaned and it takes to the sea to fend for itself.

Crabeaters are believed to live for at least 29 years.

Mutilated by killer whales

Before anything else was known of the life of crabeaters, explorers in the Antarctic had noticed that they sometimes bore huge gashes or scars running down their bodies. It is surprising that the seals could survive such injuries until it is realised that only the blubber and surface muscles are cut open, so there is no serious damage. Only one animal, the notorious killer whale, could cause such wounds and one must presume that the killer whales, who can easily kill and devour

a crabeater seal, must have been playing only half-heartedly with the seals that survived to bear the scars.

Crabeater mysteries

The survey base at Hope Bay is at the northern tip of the Antarctic Peninsula, and just to the south of it is the Crown Prince Gustav Channel that separates James Ross Island from the mainland. For most of the year the channel is frozen over and survey parties find it a convenient route for their sledging trips. In the winter of 1955 they were surprised to find vast concentrations of crabeater seals on the ice. Groups of several hundred, and one of a thousand, were counted in various parts of the channel, to make a total of 3 000 seals, ten times more than usual. More surprising was that 2 months later, in mid-October, most of these seals had died. In one large group only 3% survived. Samples of their internal organs were preserved and sent back to England where it was found that the seals had died from a disease. Some monstrous epidemic had spread through the population, creating the same sort of deathroll as myxomatosis among rabbits.

But the difference between the crabeater disease and myxomatosis is that the former has not spread through the whole population. This outbreak is an isolated instance and until more are recorded it must remain a mystery.

Another mystery is that of the skeletons and mummified bodies of crabeaters that were found 30 miles inland and 3 000 ft above sea level. For animals that are rarely found even hauled out onto beaches, this was a prodigious journey for apparently no reason. Then a few years ago a crabeater pup was found far inland. It had only recently died of starvation and bore the marks of a long journey over rocks. We can only presume that it got lost and went the wrong way as, presumably, the strays found on the shores of Australia and South America must have done.

class	Mammalia
order	Pinnipedia
family	Phocidae
genus & species	*Lobodon carcinophagus*

Crabeaters at a breathing hole in the pack ice, over which they can move at speeds of up to 15 mph.

Martin G White

Crab-eating fox

Also called the crab-eating dog, the crab-eating fox is a member of the dog family but is neither a true dog nor a true fox. This reflects a weakness in the English language, which contains names for only the three members of the dog family that have lived in the British Isles, the domesticated dog, the fox and the wolf. As a result, foreign names have been borrowed for the other members, such as coyote, or they have been given various names ending in dog, fox or wolf, depending on size or appearance.

In South America there are several members of the dog family so named, including the bush dog (p 329), and the now extinct 'Antarctic wolf' of the Falkland Islands. The crab-eating fox is certainly fox-like with a sharp muzzle, pointed ears and bushy tail. The fur is short and of varying colour, ranging from pale grey to dark brown with yellowish brown or black in parts. The ears have a dark tip. The head and body are about 2 ft long with a tail of 1 ft.

Domesticated foxes

The crab-eating fox is the common fox of Colombia and Venezuela and is found south to Peru, southeastern Bolivia, northern Argentine and Uruguay, wherever there are tropical and subtropical woods. It is found in woodland, on mountains and plains and along the banks of rivers, inhabiting areas of scattered trees as well as denser woods. This is shown in its South American names: either wood fox or *zorro de monte*.

It has been said that the crab-eating fox hunts in parties of five or six, but this is probably based on observations of family groups. It is usually solitary or hunts in pairs at night, spending the day in the abandoned burrow of some other animal.

Crab-eating foxes are sometimes caught while young by South American Indians and mated with domestic dogs to produce hybrids that are apparently very useful for hunting small animals. It has been said that the Spaniards used a similar cross for hunting hutias, a coypu-like rodent, in the West Indies. This is unlikely, however, as there are no native foxes in the West Indies.

A misleading name

The main food of the crab-eating fox is not crabs but small mammals and birds which it hunts by scent in woodlands and runs down in open country. Insects, mostly grasshoppers, frogs and lizards, are also eaten. The crab-eating fox takes fruit as well, such as figs and berries, more often than is usually appreciated. When living near rivers the crab-eating fox catches freshwater crabs—hence its name—but it also eats molluscs and other animals living in the shallows. On the plains it catches small tortoises and also digs out their eggs.

Breeding

Very little has been published on the family life of the crab-eating fox. Litters of 1—5

E Lindsey

Living paradox: although referred to as the crab-eating fox, it is neither a true dog nor a true fox, nor are crabs its main diet. A common fox in South America, it hunts small mammals and birds; it often eats insects, frogs, lizards, tortoises and their eggs, not to mention fruit. Freshwater crabs are only one of the items taken when the crab-eating fox hunts by river shallows, together with molluscs and other water creatures. It seems likely that it provides yet another example of an animal that has been given a premature name before all the facts were known—but a name which has stuck.

cubs have been born in zoos between March and August and 5 cubs, with their eyes still closed, were found in a field in September, suggesting that they are not always born in an underground den.

Not favoured by furriers

The fur is less valued than that of other South American 'dogs' and 'foxes' because of its shortness. In Buenos Aires it is marketed as 'Brazil fox' or 'provincial fox'.

Do they eat crabs?

The early naturalists are responsible for giving this fox its common English name, and at one time it was known scientifically as *Canis cancrivorus* (from Latin *cancer*—crab). They affirmed that crabs were the main item of diet and that small mammals and birds, now known to be the main food, were eaten only when crabs were not available. The fox was reputed to dive into shallow water for crabs and even recent publications show the crab-eating fox swimming down to pick a crab off the riverbed, yet authoritative scientific works make no mention of this habit. Considering the name of the fox, they would be unlikely to overlook any such observations, more especially as members of the dog family are not usually good at swimming and diving. Very little is known of the South American bush dog, for instance, yet it is known that it swims and dives well. What seems likely is that the first naturalists saw the crab-eating fox along the banks of rivers, which formed

the best, if not the only, routes through the unopened South American continent, and that they were then seen to be feeding on crabs. It would not be the first time that an animal had been given a name based on inadequate, or incorrect, knowledge.

class	**Mammalia**
order	**Carnivora**
family	**Canidae**
genus & species	***Cerdocyon thous***

Crab-eating fox *(Cerdocyon thous)*

Crab plover

The crab plover is placed in a family on its own as it is distinct from other waders both in form and habits. Its internal anatomy is like that of true plovers.

An unusual wader, about 15 in. long, it has conspicuous black and white plumage. Most of the body is white but the flight feathers and the back are black, so the crab plover resembles an avocet. The legs are long and the toes are partially webbed. The tail is short and the black bill is fairly long, powerful and heron-like.

Crab plovers are found on shores and on reefs around the coasts of the Indian Ocean, from Natal, in South Africa, and Madagascar around to the Andaman Islands, in the eastern Indian Ocean, and including the Red Sea and the Persian Gulf. They are only visitors in the southern parts of their range, going there after breeding on the shores from Somalia to the Andaman Islands.

Noisy and fearless

Crab plovers are noisy birds and quite tame, unlike many other waders. Outside the breeding season they are found in flocks and have been seen perching on hippopotamuses as they lie in the water. A flock may consist of several hundred crab plovers which fly or stand in tight formations making a raucous din that can be heard a mile or more away. Colonel Meinertzhagen, who contributed much to our knowledge of birds in the Red Sea and Persian Gulf area, has described his difficulty in obtaining a pair of crab plovers for museum specimens. He had the greatest difficulty in shooting two birds without injuring many others. Eventually one shot killed four crab plovers, but instead of the flock flying away, it gathered around the dead birds while individual members tried to rescue their companions by pushing them along. They flew away only when Meinertzhagen was 10 yd away, showing a disregard for humans quite unlike other waders, which may flee as soon as anyone comes in sight.

Feeding on the strandline

Crab plovers feed along the shore seeking out marine animals as they become stranded and exposed by the ebbing tide. They are aptly named, for their main prey is crabs. These are caught in the bill and banged against the ground until unable to escape. Small crabs are then swallowed whole and large ones ripped apart and eaten piecemeal. Worms, crustaceans and fish spawn are also eaten, as are shellfish which are first battered to crack them open.

Nesting in holes

The breeding habits of crab plovers are unlike those of other waders, for they nest in burrows in sand dunes. It is during the breeding season that the crab plovers leave the shores and move a little way inland to banks and dunes protected from storms. Here the crab plovers make their burrows

The crab plover—long legs, black-and-white plumage, and a heavy, businesslike bill.

in small colonies, honeycombing the ground so it becomes difficult to walk across the colony without the ground caving in under one's feet.

The burrows are like those made by puffins and some of the petrels. The opening, which may be on level ground or in a sandy cliff or bank, leads downwards at an angle, then curves upwards and runs for 4–5 ft before ending in a nest cavity only a few inches beneath the surface. As the floor of the tunnel is beneath the level of the nest cavity there may be some protection against flooding during heavy rainstorms.

Within the nest cavity, on the bare ground, a single, large, goose-sized egg is laid, which is again unusual, for waders usually lay two to four eggs. The incubation period has not, apparently, been recorded, neither is it known whether both parents incubate. The chicks hatch with a coat of down, as do the chicks of other waders. They are also able to run shortly after hatching, but they stay in the nest cavity until fully-fledged, being fed by both parents on live crabs and other shore creatures.

A curious egg

The egg of the crab plover is worthy of attention for several reasons. For one thing it is white, whereas those of other waders, and gulls, which are also relatives of the crab plover, are noted for their speckled black or brown colours. But these birds nest in the open and their eggs must be very well camouflaged and difficult to find. On the other hand it is typical of birds nesting in tunnels or hollow trees to lay white eggs. In these situations camouflaged eggs are not necessary.

In proportion to its size the crab plover's egg is very large, a quarter of the adult's weight of 14 oz. To produce such an egg must throw considerable stress on the female, but in the long run perhaps not as much as the stress placed on birds that produce large numbers of small eggs. The crab plover is unusual, however, because, as a general rule, proportionately large eggs are produced in species where the young leave the nest shortly after hatching. In other words a large egg with plenty of food for the chick inside allows the chick to develop to an advanced stage before hatching. The crab plover is strange in that the chick is hatched in an advanced state but stays within the nest cavity.

class	**Aves**
order	**Charadriiformes**
family	**Dromadidae**
genus & species	***Dromas ardeola***

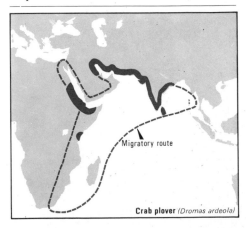

Migratory route

Crab plover *(Dromas ardeola)*

Crab spider

*Crab spiders are so called because of the length and curvature of their legs and the way they scuttle rapidly sideways, like the true crabs of the sea shore. Crab spiders are all much alike wherever they are found. Many are found in flowers, the colours of which they often match to perfection. They make no web but lie in wait for their prey. They are represented in Britain by 39 species, many rare or of local distribution, and they range from very tiny to not much more than ¼ in. All but one of these belong to the family Thomisidae, there being a single representative of the family Sparassidae, the beautiful, green **Micrommata virescens** which is comparatively large, the female being ½ in. long, the male ⅓ in.*

Beauty lies hidden

Crab spiders' colours or marks blend with their surroundings and this helps in capturing prey. Some spend most of their time in flowers, others lurk among leaf litter or low vegetation, and some lie along the stems or leaves of plants, head-downwards with the legs on each side held together in the same plane as the piece of foliage. Many combine effective camouflage with considerable beauty. *Thomisus onustus*, for example, is often a bright pink, blending perfectly with the flowers of the bell heath or certain orchids. Another, *Misumena vatia*, sometimes called the 'white death', occurs only in white or yellow plants, the white forms being found in flowers like the butterfly orchis, yellow varieties in mullein and gorse. If one of these spiders is transferred to a flower of a different colour, it quickly leaves it and seeks out another flower to match its own hue.

Danger in a flower

As the crab spider seizes its prey it pumps a poison into the victim's body along channels in its sharp-pointed jaws. This quickly affects the insect's nervous system or its blood, or both at once. The paralysed prey is then drained of its body fluids through the cuts made by the jaws. The husk is discarded. A wide variety of small insects and other invertebrates is taken.

Those crab spiders which lurk in flower heads often take insects like hover-flies, bees and butterflies which visit the flowers for nectar. Sometimes the prey is bitten in a non-fatal part, such as the abdomen, in which case the spider manipulates it until it is able to administer the *coup de grâce* in the head or thorax where the central nervous system can be more directly reached.

Captive courtship

A few days before the male undergoes his final moult he builds a small band of web on which to discharge a drop of seminal fluid. This he takes up into each of his two palps and then goes in search of a mate. There is little preliminary courtship, only tentative caressings with the legs which enable the two partners to recognise each other and which stimulate the female to

Anthony Bannister: NHPA

Two examples of crab spider technique on different-coloured flowers in the Transvaal veld: sudden death for a fly (left) and for a honey bee (above). In both cases the spider has selected a flower in which its own colour will not be noticed by the victim until too late. Crab spiders kill by striking at the victim's head and thorax.

▷ *The crab spider's hypodermic. The venom is held in the sac-like gland, which is covered with secretory cells. Muscle fibres encircle the gland; when they are contracted, venom is forced down the long duct running through the chelicera (fang).*

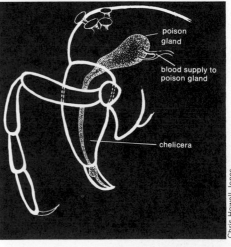

poison gland

blood supply to poison gland

chelicera

Chris Howell-Jones

△ *The face of an assassin: head-on view of a crab spider showing groups of eyes and pedipalps hiding the chelicerae or poison fangs.*
▽ *Female crab spider, with male. Like other spiders, mating is fraught with peril for the male crab spider, for the female will often seize and kill the male. In one species the male ties down the female until mating is completed and he can make good his escape.*

accept the male. Grasping the female by a leg the male inserts the sperm package in her genital aperture. If she has already mated she will not allow the male to approach but menaces him by raising her front legs and jerking her body. If he persists she may well seize and kill him. Mating may last for less than a minute or go on for several hours.

In one species *Xysticus cristatus* the male employs a device to prevent the female from seizing him. He binds her legs to the ground with threads of silk, after caressing her into accepting his initial advances. When mating is over the female is delayed just long enough in freeing herself from her bonds to allow the male to make good his escape.

Most crab spiders lay their eggs in early summer. The female makes a silken saucer into which to lay her eggs. This she then covers with another silken layer, forming a cocoon. It may be built between leaves lying on the ground or among foliage. Sometimes the female makes a silken tent within which she sits guarding the eggs. Many females eat nothing during the period of incubation, becoming extremely emaciated. Others capture prey as usual, though never straying far from their eggs. Young crab spiders are hatched as miniatures of their parents, though often differing considerably in colour. As in other spiders they grow by shedding their skins at regular intervals.

The cut-throat club

Spiders have many enemies. Small mammals, birds, reptiles and amphibians eat them, as do beetles, ants, and centipedes. Certain species of wasps and ichneumon flies lay their eggs in living crab spiders. Not least, considerable spider mortality is caused by different species of spider killing and eating one another. Indeed, it is likely that spiders indirectly play a major part in controlling their own numbers.

WS Bristowe, distinguished student of spiders, once estimated that the spider population of England and Wales alone was probably of the order of $2\frac{1}{5}$ billions (2 200 000 000 000) at any one moment—or some 40—50 thousand times the human population of Britain! If each spider eats only 100 insects a year, a conservative estimate, then the value of the service spiders render us in keeping insects down to a reasonable level is obvious. On a world scale it is incalculable.

Constance P Warner

△ *The crab spider's sharp-pointed jaws inject paralysing venom. It then drains the helpless victim of its body fluids.*

▽ *Crab spiders specialise in camouflage; this species is a perfectionist, even matching the flower's yellow-pointed stamens.*

KH Hyatt

phylum	**Arthropoda**
class	**Arachnida**
order	**Araneae**
family	**Sparassidae**
genus & species	*Micrommata virescens*
family	**Thomisidae**
genera & species	*Thomisus onustus* *Misumena vatia* others

Crake

Crakes are members of the rail family, and in North America they are known as rails. The Sora rail of America is occasionally found in Europe where it is known as the Carolina crake. The crakes are distinguished from other rails by a short conical bill.

The spotted crake is like a small corncrake, with olive-brown upper parts streaked with white and a grey, white-speckled breast. The bill is yellow with a red base. Baillon's crake, the little crake and the Carolina crake are very like the spotted crake in plumage, but the first two are much smaller, being about starling size. The ruddy crake is intermediate in size with a dark brown back, reddish brown breast and a white chin.

Ubiquitous crakes

Like their near relative the corncrake, crakes are skulking birds living in thick cover and flying only short distances, except when on migration. Their capability for sustained flight is shown by the Carolina crake's trans-Atlantic flights; at least half-a-dozen have been recorded in the British Isles. The spotted crake has made trips in the opposite direction, turning up in Greenland and the West Indies.

Crakes have a world-wide distribution and are found in Madagascar, Australia, the Philippines and many other Pacific islands as well as on the main landmasses. The spotted, little and Baillon's crakes are found in Europe and Asia, and Baillon's crake is also found in southern Africa, Australia and New Zealand—an unusual discontinuous distribution with isolated populations in different parts of the world. The Carolina crake breeds in Canada and the United States, migrating south as far as Peru in winter and occasionally reaching Britain.

Crakes are now but rarely seen in Britain. The spotted crake used to breed regularly but in the 19th century extensive drainage works destroyed its breeding grounds. Now the occasional pair breeds in England, perhaps one a year on average. Baillon's crake occasionally bred in East Anglia during the 19th century. With the little crake, Baillon's crake is now a rare visitor to Britain.

Among the rail family there is a gradation of habitat. The corncrake (p 538) prefers grassland and the coots (p 516) require open sheets of water where they can freely dive. The crakes prefer intermediate conditions, among the marshy banks of rivers and lakes and in dense reed beds where there is a sodden mat of vegetation. The Carolina crake fills the same habitat in North America as the spotted crake in Europe, which keeps to the drier borders of swamps. Baillon's crake and the little crake prefer the flooded areas in the middle of the swamps, and the little crake in particular frequents marshes with open pools.

Swamp feeding

Crakes feed on the animals and plants they can find living at the surface of the swamp

Crakes are skulking birds, living in thick cover and never flying far unless on migration. They will usually lay 6–12 eggs, and the male and the female brood them in turn for 3 weeks.

water or in the mud and decaying plants between the pools. Their main food is water snails and insects such as water beetles, mayflies and mosquitoes, as well as their larvae. Water plants and grass are also eaten. In North America, the Carolina crake eats mainly seeds during the autumn, including those of wild rice.

Father looks after firstborn

The nests are built in swamps and marshes, either on tussocks of grass or small islands, but the Carolina crake and Baillon's crake sometimes build basket-like nests in clumps of sedge or other marsh plants, a foot or more above the surface of the water. The stems of the plants around the nests are interwoven to form a canopy hiding them from possible enemies. The nest itself is made of dead rushes and grasses and is lined with finer vegetation. The Carolina crake sometimes makes a runway of nesting material, leading up to the nest.

Crakes generally lay 6–12 eggs, the spotted crake being known to lay up to 15. Male and female brood them in turn for up to 3 weeks. As incubation starts before all the eggs are laid the chicks emerge at intervals over a period of several days. They can leave the nest shortly after hatching and the male cares for them while his mate incubates the younger eggs. Then both parents guard the chicks, feeding them until they are a week old. Sometimes the chicks split into two parties, each under the charge of one parent.

Which crake is which?

Crakes are undistinguished-looking secretive birds difficult to identify at the best of times, but their preference for living in marshes with thick vegetation, water and mud, not to mention swarms of mosquitoes, makes them very difficult to observe. Probably no other group of birds in Europe is so badly known. The description of their habits given above is only a general outline as the habits of no one species is well known.

The difficulty of identification and study is best illustrated by the story of a very competent ornithologist who embarked on a study of Baillon's crakes, but years later the birds he had watched were identified from his photographs as young little crakes. Since then Baillon's crakes have been identified in various parts of Europe by comparing their calls with a recording made in 1948. But in 1968 a bird making a call similar to this recording was trapped and found to be a female little crake.

class	**Aves**
order	**Gruiformes**
family	**Rallidae**
genus & species	***Porzana porzana*** spotted crake ***P. carolina*** Carolina crake ***P. parva*** little crake ***P. pusilla*** Baillon's crake, others

One of the most impressive cranes of all: the crowned crane, with its Roman-helmet crest, gives a good idea of how head and neck coloration can often be used to pick out the different crane species.

Crane

An elegant, long-legged, long-necked heron-like bird, the largest crane stands 5 ft high, with a wingspan of 7½ ft. There are 14 kinds of these impressive birds, most of them now rare. As they are very wary, disturbance of the cranes' habitat has caused their decline as much as hunting, but it seems that within historical times some species were never numerous.

Species are often distinguished by the patches of colour around head and neck. The common crane has a red crown with black and white on head and neck. The whooping, sandhill and sarus cranes and the brolga have red patches on the head. The crowned crane is often said to be the most striking. It has white ovals behind the eyes, a red wattle and a plume of orange-brown feathers, like the crest on a Roman helmet. Yet few birds can be more impressive than the Manchurian crane, with its starkly contrasting black and white plumage. The head and neck are black except for a white patch on the crown reaching to the eyes. The body is pure white except for the black secondaries, which form a black rear border to the wings when spread.

An unusual feature of cranes' internal anatomy is the windpipe, which may be 5 ft long, half of which is coiled within the breastbone. The enormous length of the windpipe gives the cranes their loud trombone-like calls, which carry for a mile or more.

A declining family

In many parts of the world, cranes' numbers are becoming reduced. They breed in lonely marshlands and swamps, which are becoming rarer. Shooting for sport or because the cranes damage crops has also taken a toll. The two cranes most in danger are the Manchurian crane and the whooping crane. The Manchurian crane survives in small numbers on the mainland of Siberia and in a secluded swamp on the island of Hokkaido in north Japan. The whooping crane is in a desperate plight. There were probably no more than 1 500 when Europeans arrived in America, now there are just over 40, all in one flock, and the population once went down to 22. A single disaster could annihilate them, as in 1939 when another whole flock was wiped out by a flood. Whooping cranes are particularly vulnerable, because each year they migrate from their breeding grounds in the Wood Buffalo National Park in Alberta, Canada, to a winter home on the shoreline of Texas. During this migration they have to run the gauntlet of hunters, power cables across their flight paths and other hazards, and it seems that their rate of reproduction can barely keep pace with deaths. The sandhill crane of North America is in a much better position and in places is increasing.

Apart from the sandhill and whooping cranes of North America, cranes belong to the Old World, but are not found in Madagascar, southeast Asia, New Zealand and Polynesia. The common crane lives in Europe and Asia, mainly in northern areas. In mediaeval times it was quite common in the British Isles, where it bred up to about 1600, but now only occasional visitors are seen. Yet in one week in October 1963 several hundred cranes were seen in south-ern England, and one flock of about 100 was seen near Midhurst in Sussex. These cranes were most likely to have been driven across the North Sea by bad weather.

Most cranes live in flocks and are migratory, moving from summer to winter quarters like the whooping crane described above. A migrating flock is a beautiful sight as the birds fly in V, or echelon, formation with slow, measured beats, and necks outstretched. During migration they fly at great heights, apparently up to 2 miles.

Feeding

Cranes eat mainly vegetation, including leaves, roots and fruit. Sometimes they attack crops and are persecuted for this. Overall, they probably help farmers, by eating harmful insects, thrusting their long bills into the soil to take wireworms and other larvae. Cranes also eat frogs, reptiles, small birds and mammals.

The dancing cranes

Throughout the year, but particularly in the breeding season, cranes indulge in a spectacular ritual dance. They walk around each other with quick, stiff-legged steps and wings half spread, occasionally bowing and stretching. The tempo of the dance increases, and they leap into the air, flying up 15 or more feet and drifting down in a slow-motion ballet. This dance is not confined to pairs of cranes, for sometimes whole flocks including juveniles will join together to dance — apparently from sheer high spirits. During the dance some of the cranes pick sticks or leaves with their bills, throw them into the air, and stab at them as they fall.

Cranes make their nests on the ground, piling up a heap of vegetation usually on open, marshy ground, sometimes in a few

inches of standing water. On dry ground the nest may be little more than a patch of flattened vegetation. The usual clutch is 2 eggs, the second being laid 2 days after the first, and because incubation starts immediately the first egg is laid it hatches 2 days before the second. The chick can run almost at once and, in the care of the male, leaves the nest, while the female continues to incubate the second egg. Later, when both chicks have left the nest, each may be taken care of by one parent. Their legs grow very rapidly and in one month are full grown while the wings have hardly developed. They do not fly until 9 or 10 weeks.

In Japan cranes are symbols of longevity and in folklore are reputed to live for 1 000 years. Even in real life they are known to live for at least 50 years.

The Tanchō of Hokkaido

The dance of the cranes must be one of the most spectacular performances in the bird world. Other birds have a more beautiful and elaborate plumage to set off their displays, but the cranes' size, combined with the grace and energy of their dances, makes them outstanding. Especially spectacular is the dance of a flock. The brolga of Australia, also known as the 'native companion', dances in troops lined up in rows of 20—30. The dance of the brolga is the basis for some of the dances at aboriginal corroborees, and there are crane dances in other parts of the world, where the cranes symbolise the returning spring. The aboriginal Ainu tribesmen of Japan have a dance commemorating the Tanchō or Manchurian crane.

The Manchurian crane often appears in Japanese art and literature and for hundreds of years it was protected by the Jap-

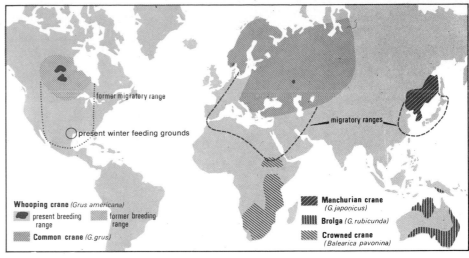

anese veneration of it as a symbol of eternal life. Only the emperor could hunt it, with goshawks, which were awarded a purple hood if they were successful in killing such a magnificent bird. The Buddhist ban on the taking of life also protected the cranes until Buddhism was ousted. Indiscriminate slaughter immediately took place, and the Manchurian cranes were exterminated in Japan except in the Kushiro swamp in Hokkaido. This swamp was inaccessible except when its waters froze, and its population of cranes did not migrate to areas where they would be more vulnerable. Nevertheless, numbers dropped to 20 in 1924, but strict preservation has allowed them to recover, and they now number about 200. In the winter they come out of the marsh and visit neighbouring farms, where the farmers feed them in return for the pleasure of seeing the cranes dance in the snow.

class	**Aves**
order	**Gruiformes**
family	**Gruidae**
genera & species	*Grus grus* common crane *G. americana* whooping crane *G. japonicus* Manchurian crane *G. rubicunda* brolga *Balearica pavonina* crowned crane others

▽ *Left: Sandhill cranes. The long, loose 'bustle', formed by the secondary wing feathers hanging over the tail, is a characteristic feature.*
Centre: Sandhill cranes show off their wing action in flight. The North American sandhills are holding their own and are on the increase in places.
Right: The colourful, high-spirited dance of a group of crowned cranes.

Joe Van Wormer: Photo Res

Simon Trevor: Photo Res

Crayfish

The crayfish is a freshwater crustacean. It looks like a small lobster, 4 in. or more long, and coloured sandy yellow, green or dark brown. The head and thorax are covered with a single shell, or carapace, which ends in front in a sharp-pointed rostrum. Its eyes are compound and stalked. On its head is a pair of small antennules which are richly supplied with sense-organs, and a pair of long antennae, which are organs of touch. These have excretory organs at the base. The crayfish has a pair of strong jaws and two pairs of smaller accessory jaws, the maxillae. The second pair of maxillae drives water over 20 pairs of feathery gills on the bases of the thoracic limbs.

Preparing to carve: a freshwater crayfish about to feed off a male stickleback.

Jane Burton: Photo Res

On the thorax there are three pairs of appendages, which are used to pass food to the jaws, a pair of stout pincers and four pairs of legs, which the crayfish uses to walk forward. The abdomen is divided into segments and has five pairs of limbs on its underside. The first pair are grooved in the males and are used to introduce sperm onto the female. The other four are swimmerets. The crayfish can swim speedily backwards with forward flicks of its abdomen, which ends in a fan-shaped tail. It does this to escape.

Crayfish in cooler waters

The two families of crayfish are confined almost entirely to temperate regions: the Potamobiidae in the northern hemisphere, the Parastacidae in the southern hemisphere. There are no crayfish in Africa, but they are present in Madagascar. There is none in the greater part of Asia, but they are found in Korea and the northern islands of Japan. The largest crayfish *Astacopsis franklinii* lives in Tasmania and may weigh up to 9 lb. Another large crayfish related to it is sold as Murray River Lobster in southeastern Australia. One of the Tasmanian crayfish, known as a land crab, habitually leaves the water and burrows in damp earth in forests. In the Mammoth Cave in Kentucky, in the United States, there are several crayfish living in the underground waters. They are colourless and blind; the eyes are gone, leaving only the stalks.

Naturalized aliens

Only one crayfish *Potamobius pallipes* is native to Britain. It is known as the white claw. A larger European crayfish *Astacus fluviatilis*, reared on farms especially in France, has been introduced into the Thames, and is known as the red claw. An American species, introduced into Germany, has become established there. The three species have similar habits. They live in rivers and lakes, especially those with hard water which contains the lime needed for their shell. They feed mainly at night, resting by day in burrows in the mud or under stones, but can sometimes be seen moving about by day.

They eat smaller aquatic animals such as insect larvae, snails, worms and tadpoles, and a small amount of plant food. In the Mississippi Valley they graze on rice during the night. This infuriates the local farmers who regard them as pests.

Unusual breeding habits

Crayfish mate in the autumn. The male turns the female over and sheds milt through the first pair of abdominal appendages onto her abdomen, where it sticks. The female then goes into a burrow to lay her hundred or so eggs. These become attached to bristles on her swimmerets where they are fertilised by contact with the milt. The eggs hatch the following spring. Unusual for a crustacean there is no larval stage. The newly-hatched crayfish are transparent, and tiny replicas of the adults. They remain attached for some time to the female's swimmerets, which they grasp with their claws.

Life and death in crayfish

In many parts of the world, crayfish are considered a delicacy. Sometimes they are eaten raw although this can prove to be hazardous, because crayfish carry a fluke larva. If this is swallowed with a crayfish it will migrate through the wall of the gut to the lungs, where it matures to the adult parasite. In time the adult lays eggs which are ejected with the sputum. From the eggs hatch first stage larvae which infest snails. The cycle of parasitic infection is completed if a snail is eaten by a crayfish.

One interesting aspect of the life of a crayfish is that it grows by periodic moults. This is common knowledge and is often stated in books on natural history. Most crustaceans and insects grow like this. But although it is always stated simply, the process itself is complex. In crayfish it takes place in four stages. First the calcium salts, the chalky matter in the old shell, are taken back into the blood, ready to be laid down again in the new shell being formed beneath the old one. Then the old shell, or such as remains of it, now merely a tough cuticle, is shed and the body takes up water and swells. Then the calcium salts are laid down in the new cuticle and this takes time to harden.

The moult of a crayfish takes 6 hours. During this time the crayfish fasts and stays in hiding. It is a very dangerous period for it; not only is it vulnerable especially to enemies, but it is also in danger from the many attendant difficulties of the process itself. It has only recently been realized, in fact, that many crayfish die during this complicated moulting process.

phylum	**Arthropoda**
class	**Crustacea**
order	**Decapoda**
families	**Parastacidae**
	Potamobiidae
genera & species	*Astacus fluviatilis* *Potamobius pallipes* *others*

△ Male and female freshwater crayfish. Notice the egg clusters on the female (right), attached to bristles on her swimmerets. Crayfish mate in the autumn, and the eggs hatch in the following spring. Unlike most other crustaceans there is no larval stage: the young are tiny replicas of the adults.

▽ Transparent, fragile crayfish babies cling to the swimmerets of their mother. Crayfish grow by periodic moults, each lasting 6 hours.

Creeper

The treecreepers are among several groups of birds called creepers, including the Australian treecreepers, the wallcreeper that is related to the nuthatch, and various members of the antbird, babbler and ovenbird families. Treecreepers, or simply creepers, as they are known in North America, a term to be preferred because it is more embracing, are sparrow-sized birds with brown, streaked plumage on the back and light underparts. They have slender, pointed bills and long curved claws. The tail looks tattered, as it is made up of stiff pointed feathers.

The common treecreeper ranges from the British Isles to Japan, and in North America, where it is known as the brown-creeper, from Alaska to Nicaragua.

John Markham

Farther south it is replaced by the very similar woodcreepers. The short-toed treecreeper is also found in much of Europe, except the British Isles and Scandinavia, and spreads into Turkey and North Africa. Where the two species overlap, the short-toed treecreeper stays mainly in deciduous, broad-leaved woodland, while the common treecreeper lives in conifer forests. It has been suggested that the short-toed treecreeper does not live in the British Isles because it followed the spread of the broad-leaved trees as they moved north through Europe after the Ice Age. Before the short-toed tree-creeper reached the British Isles, the common treecreeper had already arrived

in the wake of the conifers. The Straits of Dover then opened up, and the common treecreeper adapted itself to broad-leaved trees, as there was no competition from the short-toed treecreeper. The remaining three creepers live in the Himalayan region.

Creepers live on tree trunks

Creepers are woodland birds. They are not strong fliers, and are usually seen flitting from one tree to another or hopping jerkily up a tree trunk, peering from side to side in search of food, in the same way as nuthatches. The two are readily distinguishable by their plumage, and the creepers nearly always hop up the trunk, and when they descend go down backwards, rather than headfirst like a nuthatch. Creepers also use their stiff tail as a support, pressing it against the trunk, like a woodpecker.

At night, creepers roost in crevices in bark, under eaves, in ivy or in holes in dead or soft-barked trees, where they fluff out their feathers to keep warm. Sometimes groups of about 15 at a time will huddle together in a fluffy ball on cold nights, but at other times they show strict ownership, and a creeper will attack others that it finds in its roost.

Food found in bark

As a creeper climbs up a tree or along a branch it searches for insects, spiders and woodlice, together with their eggs and larvae, which it pulls out of crevices with its finely pointed bill. Seeds are very occasionally eaten. The bark of the tree is searched systematically; the creeper starts at the base and works spirally upwards. If it finds a particularly rewarding section it flutters down and goes over it again. When

one tree has been searched, the creeper flies to the base of the next.

Spiral courtship chase

Creepers' songs are very high-pitched thin trills, and so are as relatively inaudible to our ears as the birds are inconspicuous to our eyes. During courtship the male chases the female in spirals around tree trunks, or flies in spirals around the trunk where she is perching.

The nest of the common treecreeper, that is the North American browncreeper, is made in the same places as the roosts. It is an untidy mass of grass, moss and leaves, with a cup-shaped depression at the centre lined with feathers and bark.

The 4–7 eggs, usually 5, are incubated by the female alone, at least in North America. It seems that in Europe the male sometimes helps in incubation, although he does not have the featherless brood patch on his breast. Incubation lasts 15 days and the chicks spend a further 15 in the nest, being fed by both parents.

Creepers' roosts

In the 19th century there was a fashion in the British Isles for planting exotic trees and shrubs, with the result that Wellingtonias, monkey-puzzle trees and rhododendrons are now quite common in many parts of the country. In Scotland, in 1905, and in England a few years later, treecreepers were found to be making roosts in Wellingtonias by digging holes in the trunks about 2½ in. diameter and 2 in. deep. Wellingtonia bark is soft and spongy. It is possible to punch it with all one's might and not hurt the knuckles, and creepers are able to peck holes easily.

The habit of making roosting holes in Wellingtonias spread rapidly through the country from 1930 onwards, and it is likely that this happened for two reasons. Creepers will dig holes in the soft wood of dead trees, and in California the browncreepers make holes in the native Wellingtonias and incense cedars. They prefer older trees with rough bark and it was during the early part of this century that the Wellingtonias planted in the British Isles were becoming rough. At the same time farmers and foresters no longer tolerated dead trees, so depriving treecreepers of their original roosting sites.

It is not difficult to see a creeper in its roosting hole if one knows where to find the hole. If this is being currently used there will be an accumulation of droppings on the bark under it. The creeper retires to rest at dusk, fitting neatly into the hole with tail hanging out, feathers fluffed and beak buried in its shoulder feathers. Once it has gone to sleep, it is quite easily seen with the aid of a torch.

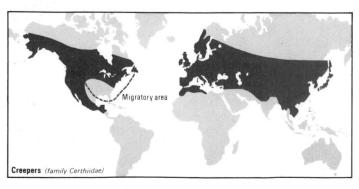

Creepers (family Certhiidae)

Above: Hooked onto the tree face by its long curved claws, a treecreeper leans across to feed its young.

class	**Aves**
order	**Passeriformes**
family	**Certhiidae**
genus & species	***Certhia familiaris*** treecreeper or browncreeper ***C. brachydactyla*** short-toed treecreeper others

Crested lark

The crested lark is a little smaller than a skylark, measuring 6¾ in. from head to tail. Several larks have crests, but these are not as conspicuous as those of the crested lark or the very similar thekla lark. Some ornithologists have placed these two larks in the same species, but it is now generally accepted that they are sufficiently distinct to be kept apart. It is very difficult to tell them apart in the field however. The thekla lark is smaller with shorter and narrower wings and it has a distinctly shorter and less pointed bill than the crested lark. The crest on the latter is reported to be more of a spike of feathers while that of the thekla lark consists of a complete fan. The two birds also have different songs.

Feeding

The crested lark lives mainly on grain, from oats and wheat and the seeds of grasses and weeds. During the winter it is not above picking the undigested grains out of horse droppings. In the breeding season, when it has a family of hungry chicks to feed, it catches beetles, grasshoppers and larvae.

Chicks sheltered from the sun

The song of the crested lark, a liquid whistle of three or four syllables, is like that of a skylark but is not so loud or continuous. Like the skylark, the crested lark sings high in the air, from as much as 100—200 ft up. It does not sing, however, while ascending or descending, so it is not so conspicuous as the skylark which rises slowly, singing all the time. The crested lark also sings while perched on houses, trees or telephone wires.

The nest is built by both sexes from grass stems which are woven into a cup and lined

plumage with samples of the sandy soil on which they live has shown that the plumage tends to match the different soils. The matching shades enable the larks to merge against their background. This protects them from being spotted by enemies.

Crested and thekla larks that live in semi-desert areas match their surroundings particularly well. In one test 25 larks out of 33 were found to match the colour of the soil where they were living. This figure improved to 20 out of 22 when comparisons were made in the breeding season only. This suggests that the larks are especially adapted to suit the background colour of their breeding habitat, which would obviously have the most survival value. In Europe, however, the match is not so good; only 8 larks out of 14 matched the soil. This is probably because the vegetation is thicker than in North Africa and the larks' nests are not surrounded by bare soil.

Camouflage like this is not confined to the

Peter Johnson

The crested lark is only rarely found in the British Isles, when it comes over from the Continent. Its breeding range extends from the Atlantic coasts of France and Spain to Korea and covers northern India, Arabia, and North Africa, around the fringes of the Sahara, down the Red Sea coast to Ethiopia and Somalia. In historical times it spread up through Europe from the Mediterranean and between 1850 and 1900 it colonised parts of Scandinavia. It is now found in Denmark and nearby parts of Norway and Sweden. The thekla lark is found in Spain, North Africa (from Mauretania to Egypt) and in Ethiopia and Somalia. Where their ranges overlap the two larks generally breed in different habitats.

Bird of desert fringes

The crested lark usually lives on flat, rather barren, steppe country and the fringes of deserts where there are patches of sandy soil with coarse grass and low, thorny bushes. It is also common along roadsides, in gardens, and on waste land in towns. As the steppes of central Europe became cultivated it spread through the continents as other suitable habitats were formed along roads and railways that were being built.

with rootlets or hair. The nests are under low bushes or in thick grass, but sometimes on roofs of sheds or houses. Usually they are sheltered from the glare of the midday sun and sometimes a dome is woven over the nest cup.

In Europe, 4 or 5 eggs are laid; in Africa and Asia Minor 5 or 6.

The female incubates the eggs

Incubation is by the female alone. In hot weather she does not sit on the eggs, but stands over them, sheltering them from the sun's heat. After the chicks have emerged, the female lark eats the eggshells or drops them 1 or 2 ft from the nest. The eggs hatch in 11—12 days and the chicks stay in the nest for a week or more, but they do not fly for at least another week.

Camouflaged larks

With the exception of the male black lark, members of the lark family have a brown plumage, streaked with grey or buff. The underparts are lighter and more uniform. When perched or feeding on the ground, or sitting on the nest, they are very hard to see. Most animals are inconspicuous when motionless, whatever their colour, but the larks, living in sparsely-vegetated margins of deserts, blend in particularly well with their background. Comparison of their

Arthur Christiansen

Left: Feeding time for a crested lark family. Larks will normally nest on the ground, weaving grass stalks into a cup for the eggs, but they will sometimes nest on the roof of a shed or house. Crested larks lay 4 or 5 eggs in Europe, 5 or 6 in Africa and Asia Minor.
Above: Winter and rough weather: a crested lark dourly faces winter conditions by fluffing up its feathers to trap air for warmth. Although the wings of the crested lark are shorter than those of the skylark, the crested lark's wing area is considerably larger.

crested and thekla larks. Over their range, from North Africa eastwards, the plumage of sand larks also closely matches the various soil colours. In Arabia, for instance, where there are patches of black lava in the pale sand, there are two races of desert lark. The dark race lives on the lava and the light race on the sand. No amount of chasing will make them run on to ground of the wrong colour.

class	**Aves**
order	**Passeriformes**
family	**Alaudidae**
genus	***Galerida cristata*** crested lark
& species	**G. thekla** thekla lark

Crested porcupine

The porcupines of the Old World do not climb. Porcupines of the New World spend much time in trees. For this reason, and because of other differences, New World porcupines are placed in a separate family, which will be dealt with under tree porcupine.

One of the largest of the rodents, the crested porcupine is up to 28 in. long exclusive of its 5in. tail, and it may weigh up to 60 lb. It is brownish-black with a whitish band around the neck, and is heavily built with short stout legs. The body is covered with two kinds of quills; one set is short and stout, the other long and slender, and both are banded black and white. The long quills may be over 1 ft long and $\frac{1}{4}$ in. diameter. On the head and neck is a crest of long white bristles with brown bases. The quills on the rump are black, those on the tail are white.

The crested porcupine ranges across North Africa, from Morocco to the Sudan and southern Egypt, and is also found south of the Sahara from Senegal to tropical eastern Africa. It also occurs in Sicily and Italy, where it was probably introduced, and has recently been introduced into Albania and southern Yugoslavia. It is one of 8 species of Hystrix, *all similar, distributed from South Africa through southern Asia to Indonesia. There are 7 more related species, 2 similar to* Hystrix, *4 species of brush-tailed porcupines in Africa, and 1 long-tailed porcupine in Borneo and Sumatra.*

Vegetarians that gnaw bones

Despite their strange spiny appearance porcupines are rodents and their quills are merely modified hairs. As with all rodents they have a pair of stout chisel-like incisor teeth in both upper and lower jaws. They grow continuously at the roots and need constant use, not only to keep them sharp but also to wear them down at the crowns to prevent them growing too long. This partly accounts for the porcupine habit of gnawing bones. Doubtless they also benefit from the lime and phosphorus salts in the bone.

Porcupines live singly or at most in pairs. They live chiefly on rocky hills with good undergrowth and spend the day in holes in the ground or among rocks, coming out at night to feed on roots, bulbs, bark and fallen fruits. Near cultivated land they can become a pest to crops.

Born with soft quills

Breeding takes place early in the year and, after a gestation of 63–112 days, 2–3 babies are born fully developed in a nest of leaves, grass and roots. Their eyes are open at birth and the quills are soft and flexible, but harden within the next 10 days. The young are at first striped black and white. In captivity porcupines have lived up to 20 years or slightly more.

Dreaded pincushion

It is doubtful whether porcupines suffer seriously from enemies. Only the larger carnivores such as leopards and hunting dogs can successfully attack them, and even these do so usually when very hungry and probably desperate. They can more easily take the young, and experienced predators learn to flip a porcupine over and attack the soft underbelly. There are stories from Africa of lions, and more particularly elderly lionesses with cubs to feed, who have tried conclusions with porcupines as age or damaged teeth prevented their killing more rapidly moving prey. Even so, they have paid for it with quills painfully embedded in the mouth or paws.

A porcupine's defence is to raise and spread its quills, rattle them to give warning of attack and then to rush backwards at the enemy. The quills are only loosely embedded in the skin so they easily become detached and embedded in the enemy's flesh. After that, because of their barbed points, any movement causes them to work their way in deeper and deeper, and they have been known to end up in the heart or some other vital organ.

The main danger to porcupines is that man eats their flesh. Africans, especially, catch porcupines for food, and the animals have little defence against them.

Do they shoot their quills?

There is a well-established story that a porcupine will shoot its quills at an enemy, and many zoologists have been at pains to explain that this is nonsense. The best explanation given so far comes from the American naturalist, William J Long, when writing of the North American porcupine, which we shall be dealing with under tree porcupine. He has described how one night he rolled rocks towards a porcupine on the ground to see how it would react. He saw the porcupine flick its tail in a sidewise blow, and later he found quills that were broken in hitting the rock. He also tells of a woodsman trying to tame a porcupine. In the morning he used to find quills outside the wire-netting of the cage, evidence perhaps of a roving dog having startled the porcupine. In these and other instances Long quotes he assumes that the porcupine's natural reaction to an intruder is to flick its tail sharply, throwing off loose quills.

Although these explanations for an old story come from the New World, the story itself originated in the Old World and was probably first associated with the crested porcupine. It is of interest that the story as it is usually told today is of the porcupine deliberately shooting its quills. We cannot blame our forefathers for this because if we turn to the 15th-century natural history book, the *Hortus Sanitatis*, we read merely that the porcupine 'looses its spines from its back'. The rest has been added later. For example, in Churchill's *Voyages* (1744) we read 'if they are vexed they can by contracting themselves cast [their quills] forth with such strength that they kill man or beast'.

Cuddly companion

The brushtailed porcupines look smaller than the crested porcupines largely because their quills are shorter. Their tails are, however, longer, with a tuft of quills at the end. A story from Sierra Leone tells of a young pet brushtailed porcupine, hand-reared and allowed the run of the bungalow. It had been given a piece of soft cloth in the corner of a room. It seemed content for a few days, then became restless and uneasy. In due course it found its way to the bathroom, discovered the lavatory brush, with bristles almost as stout as its own quills, took this to its sleeping place and nestled beside it, content. Was it missing its mother?

En garde: sensing danger, a cornered porcupine raises its spines. In dealing with attacks, the 'killer punch' of the porcupine is the accurate, sideways slap of its spine-armoured tail.

Jane Burton: Photo Res

class	**Mammalia**
order	**Rodentia**
family	**Hystricidae**
genera & species	*Hystrix cristata* *Atherurus africanus* *others*

Anthony Maynard

The crested swift **Hemiprocne longipennis**

Crested swift

A family of swifts not so completely adapted for aerial life as the true swifts. The crested swifts are in some ways more like swallows. The tail is deeply forked, and the plumage soft and swallow-like rather than coarse and swift-like. They have stronger legs and can perch readily on twigs and branches, but cannot turn one toe back so that two face forwards and two backwards as in true swifts. The conspicuous crest at the base of the bill is raised when the swift is on the nest or calling, but is flattened in flight.

There are three species of crested swift. The common species is a pretty bird, 8 in. long. Its back, wings and head, including the crest, vary from an iridescent dark green to ash grey. The throat is light grey fading to white towards the belly. Male can be distinguished from female by a rufous patch on each cheek. The two other species have white plumes above and below the eye.

Singapore garden bird
Crested swifts are noisy birds, flying about in small parties, continually calling to each other. They are more manoeuvrable in flight than other swifts, which may be a reason why they frequent wooded, rather than open, places. They are more active during the day than other swifts in the same area, which are seen more in the evening. Crested swifts are found in southeast Asia and across the Pacific, ranging from India to the Solomon Islands. They are common throughout the Federation of Malaya and in Singapore. Seldom seen in treeless country, they are found in forests, mangrove swamps, rubber plantations and gardens. Recently crested swifts have become town birds, and are now common in Singapore City, for instance.

Fly hunters
Crested swifts feed on small flying insects such as flies and gnats. They do not continu-ally fly about like the true swifts but tend to perch in small flocks, each flying off to catch an insect and returning to the perch, rather in the manner of a flycatcher.

A frail nest
The breeding habits of crested swifts are not very well known, but this may be changed now they are coming more into built-up areas. Prior to this, one found a crested swift's nest only by many patient hours of peering through binoculars, following the birds until one was seen to land on its nest. Two difficulties prevent the nests from being found easily. They are usually built high above ground, perhaps 45 ft or more, and although built on a bare branch, are minute and very difficult to see unless one knows where to look.

The nest is a shelf fixed to the side or top of a branch, $1\frac{1}{2}-2$ in. long and $\frac{1}{2}-\frac{3}{4}$ in. wide. The shelf is curved up to form a bowl about $\frac{1}{2}$ in. deep, and is made out of thickened saliva mixed with feathers. To make the nest more difficult to see, the bottom may be camouflaged with small pieces of bark that the swift tears from trees.

In this nest, an egg nearly 1 in. long and just over $\frac{1}{2}$ in. diameter is laid and glued in place with saliva. Both sexes incubate it, but it is impossible for them to sit on it in the normal way without the nest tearing away from the branch. Instead, the swift sits on the branch just beside the nest and fluffs its breast feathers over the egg, so it looks as if it is wearing a cape. Nest building and egg-laying have not been observed, and it would be difficult to do so closely because, even if a pair were found in the early stages of nest building, a hide on a scaffolding would have to be built alongside to get a closer look. Because of this difficulty the incubation period is unknown. Once the egg has been laid, however, observation is very easy and one ornithologist found the parents sat so tight that he had to push them aside to see the egg or chick.

The chick spends a week sitting in the nest, during which time it grows a coat of down that camouflages it so well that it looks like a lichen-covered projection of the branch. It spends the second week, before it starts to fly, sitting on the branch beside the nest which is now too small to hold it. Both parents feed the chick, bringing back insects which it takes by putting its bill inside that of the parent.

Precarious upbringing
The swifts are noted for the precarious way in which they rear their young. The palm swift merely glues its egg to a palm leaf, but even the relatively solid construction of the crested swift poses some problems. First it would be interesting to see how the female lays the egg. She would have to be very careful to see that it did not drop from too great a height or else the nest might collapse. Next, there is the problem that once the egg is cemented in, it cannot be turned as the eggs of other birds are turned at regular intervals to ensure that they are warmed evenly. Presumably, in the tropical home of the crested swift this is not so important and the parent bird sitting over the nest may be to keep the egg cool. It would also be interesting to see how the chick emerges from the egg. This is usually no easy task as the emerging chick is limp and can only wriggle feebly. The crested swift's nest is hardly large enough for both chick and eggshell. Perhaps the adult assists the chick in its manoeuvres.

Whatever the answers are to these problems, this type of nesting must be efficient. Crested swifts lay only one egg at a time and, remembering the other hazards that eggs and young birds face, extra dangers of egg or chick falling from the nest would prevent the crested swifts from being as common as they are.

class	**Aves**
order	**Apodiformes**
family	**Hemiprocnidae**
genus & species	*Hemiprocne longipennis* others

547

Cricket

There are 900 species of cricket, found throughout the world except in polar regions. Apart from the mole crickets, of which there are two species, one in Europe and another in North America, the various kinds differ only slightly. The smallest members are wingless, $\frac{1}{5}$ in. long, and they live in ants' nests, feeding on the ants' oil secretions. These crickets are found only in parts of the northern hemisphere.

Typical crickets resemble grasshoppers and locusts and also the bush crickets, sometimes called long-horned grasshoppers or, in America, katydids. All have long hindlegs used for jumping. Crickets differ from grasshoppers, but resemble bush crickets, in having long, thread-like antennae. They produce sound in the same way as bush crickets and, like them, have hearing organs, or 'ears', in the form of a pit on each front leg. Crickets hold their wings flat over the back with the edges sharply bent down at the sides, and there is a pair of jointed appendages, or cerci, at the tip of the abdomen. The female carries a stiff tubular ovipositor through which the eggs are laid. Most crickets are black or brown in colour.

Crickets for all situations

The house cricket has been spread all over the world by man but is probably a native of North Africa and southwest Asia. In temperate climates it can live only indoors or in rotting refuse heaps which give continual warmth. It is brown, a little over $\frac{1}{2}$ in. long, has fully developed wings and long, angled hindlegs. It hides by day and comes out at night to look for scraps of food, when the males make their small chirping song to attract females. The field cricket, once common in southern England but now rare, ranges across Europe to North Africa. Nearly 1 in. long, shiny black with pale yellow markings at the bases of the forewings, it has a large head, compared with the body. The hindwings are so reduced that field crickets cannot fly. They live on heaths, preferring warm south-facing slopes. The adults hibernate in burrows dug with their large powerful jaws. The wood cricket, small and brown, less than $\frac{1}{2}$ in. long, ranges across the southern half of Europe, into western Asia and North Africa. It is found sparingly in a few southern English counties. It has no hindwings and cannot fly.

The mole cricket, once common, but now very rare in Britain, is found all over Europe, western Asia and North Africa. Dark brown and covered with a fine velvety hair, it is $1\frac{1}{2}$ in. long and lacks the long jumping hindlegs of a typical cricket. Its forelegs are modified for digging, and in action they look much like the forelegs of a mole. The hindwings are fully developed and mole crickets fly about freely.

The scaly cricket of the Mediterranean area seems to be found at only one point in the British Isles, at Chesil Beach, Dorset.

Colin G Butler

△ Adult wood crickets (female at right). Female crickets are distinguished by their long ovipositor.
▽ Female tree cricket: this is one of the bush crickets or long-horned grasshoppers. The ovipositor of the bush cricket is sabre-like and curves upward. In true crickets it is straight and lance-like.

Keystone

The heavy-bodied, short-winged mole cricket has powerful front legs, well equipped for digging, and armed with cutting edges for dealing with rootlets. It drives long, shallow tunnels just below the surface—and despite its subterranean tastes it is a perfectly capable flier.

Colin G Butler

This has probably been introduced from ships calling at Portland Harbour.

Eat almost anything

Crickets are mainly vegetarian but will take insect food, the proportion varying not only with the species but with circumstances. They will eat dead animal food as well as household scraps. This omnivorous diet has made it easy for the house cricket to live alongside man, and it has given, falsely, a bad reputation to the mole cricket. This is often regarded as a pest and it can sometimes do damage to root crops, but for the most part it feeds on insects.

Calling for mates

The sound of the cricket, once welcome, tends today to be regarded as a nuisance. It is produced by stridulation, rubbing the finely toothed vein on the right forewing against the hind edge of the left forewing. A clear area on the left wing acts as a resonator. The male sits at the mouth of his burrow singing while the female wanders about, guided by his song, until she finds him. Female crickets become excited after they hear the song of a male through a telephone, showing that it is to this song and not to scent or sight of the male that they react.

The male cricket deposits his sperm in small capsules, known as spermatophores, which are taken up by the female.

The field cricket lays her eggs during the summer by inserting them into the ground with her ovipositor. The young hatch fully grown the following spring, after hiber-

▽ *The sound mechanism of the cricket*
It is produced by the rapid friction of the cricket's wings—like a man rubbing his hands together. The finely-toothed file vein on the underside of the right forewing is rubbed against the scraper on the hind edge of the left forewing. The bottom illustration shows the overlapping action of the wings during the cricket's song. This song is, in every sense of the word, a love song. Experiments have shown that it is the song—not the scent or the sight of the male—which excites the female cricket.

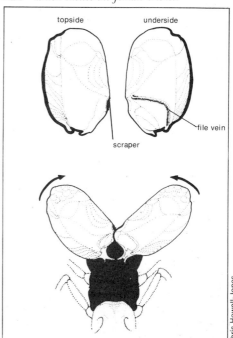

topside   underside

file vein

scraper

Chris Howell-Jones

△ *Superb camouflage: the sharply-jointed legs of a bush cricket in the field blend perfectly with the angles of the surrounding vegetation.*

▽ *The startling colour of a bush cricket's face. Unlike grasshoppers, crickets and bush crickets have long, thread-like sensitive antennae.*

nation. The adults die in July and August. The wood cricket lays her eggs in autumn, the young hatching the following spring and hibernating to complete their growth in the second summer. Consequently adults of one year can never meet adults of the year immediately past or following. This has led to 'even-year' and 'odd-year' wood crickets which seem to be different races biologically isolated from each other.

The mole cricket lays her eggs in spring in an underground nest and remains with them for up to 2 weeks until they hatch.

The thermometer cricket

The American tree crickets of the genus *Oecanthus* are very sensitive to temperature when singing. The rate of the chirps is speeded up as the temperature rises so exactly that the temperature in degrees Fahrenheit can be calculated quite accurately by timing them. You tell the temperature by counting the number of chirps in 15 seconds and adding 39. If you have a thermometer and no watch, the cricket can be used as a timer: just multiply the temperature by 4 and subtract 160 to find the number of chirps uttered per minute.

Chinese cricket matches

The Chinese have long had an interest in and sympathy for insects, which is reflected in their art. Crickets especially fascinated them by their singing and their pugnacity. Many varieties have been selectively bred for their musical qualities, and others have been specially bred for fighting. Both were kept in small bamboo cages.

The points looked for in a fighting cricket were loud chirping, big head, long legs, and broad backs. Successful fighters were pampered pets fed on special foods including a soup made from a special flower and mosquitoes gorged with blood from their owner's arm. But they were starved before a fight to step up their fighting spirit.

Fights were staged in special bowls on tables with silk covers. A referee recited the past deeds of the contestants before encouraging them to fight by prodding them with a fine hair. Bets were laid and the end usually came when one cricket bit off the other's head, to earn the victor an entry in letters of gold on an ivory scroll, as *shou lip* (conquering cricket).

At first cricket fighting was the costly pastime of the leisurely scholar of Imperial times. Later it became an entertainment of less literate people. Even 30 years ago the 'sport' had degenerated to little better than an amusing old custom, rapidly dying out. Today it is played only by children.

phylum	**Arthropoda**
class	**Insecta**
order	**Orthoptera**
family	**Gryllidae**
genera & species	***Acheta domesticus*** *house cricket* ***Gryllus campestris*** *field cricket* ***Nemobius sylvestris*** *wood cricket* ***Gryllotalpa gryllotalpa*** *mole cricket* *others*

John Tashjian at Scripps Inst

Yellowfin croakers. Apart from their extraordinary capacity for sound output, croakers are fairly ordinary carnivorous fishes with almost-touching twin dorsal fins.

Croaker

Croaker is the name given to 160 species of the family of North American fishes, remarkable for the noises they make. Some of them have been called drums or drumfishes. They usually have a rounded snout, two dorsal fins almost joining, the front part being spiny. Some have a number of small barbels under the chin. Most of them are used as food-fishes. One known as the channel bass is over 4 ft long with a weight of up to 83 lb although most of them are only a few pounds in weight.

The Atlantic croaker is well known from Massachusetts to Argentina. These are fairly ordinary carnivorous fishes laying small eggs which, since each contains an oil globule, float at the surface.

Submarine choristers

By far the most spectacular feature of these fishes is the way in which their noises are used like bird song. They are not the only fishes to do this, but as a family they are outstanding in their performances. The sounds are made in most instances by the vibration of muscles with the swimbladder acting as resonator. Sometimes the muscles are attached directly to the surface of the swimbladder, in other species the muscles are attached to the body wall. In all the use is similar: by contraction and relaxation, at a rate of about 24 contractions a second, the muscle is made to vibrate almost like the strings of a guitar. The sounds have been variously described as drumming, hum-

ming, purring, whistling, creaking, croaking, hissing, snorting, even a 'melodious vocal effort'. In some the sounds are relatively feeble, but the loudest of the croakers has been heard by a person, 6 ft above the surface of the sea on the deck of a boat, while the fish was calling from a depth of nearly 60 ft. In Malaya fishermen locate the fish by their sounds.

Fishes not deaf

It used to be argued that fishes are unable to hear, just as it used to be supposed they made no sounds. Fishes in which the swimbladder is not directly connected to the bones of the inner ear can respond to frequencies between 13 and 2 000—3 000 cycles per second. Where there is a connection they can respond to frequencies between 16 and 10 000 cps. The noises they make are well within these ranges, but are mainly low notes.

The sounds are put to many uses in different species of fishes: to enable members of a shoal to keep in touch, possibly as an echosounder for depth, for breeding and as an expression of emotions. Illustrating the last of these we have the experience in a public aquarium in the United States. Visitors could, by pressing a button, hear yellowfin and spotfin croakers 'talking' in one of the tanks. All went well until the fishes had settled in and felt at home, when they ceased being loquacious—and visitors had to be content with a recording.

Million-strong choir

The evidence for the other uses is equally scanty and this study is as yet in its infancy. As to members of a shoal keeping in touch,

we have observations of the kind recorded for croakers living in the seas around Japan. These are known to assemble in large schools of up to a million and synchronize their drumming. In many species of croakers the volume of sound given out increases as the breeding season approaches, reaches a peak during it, and dies out afterwards. In a few species the sounds begin in the evening, reaching a high pitch towards midnight then sharply dying away. It has been shown by close observation that some species have a dawn chorus, others have both dawn and dusk choruses. In some species only the males 'croak', in others both sexes do so. All this is so like what is found in birds that it seems reasonable the croakers are using their 'guitars' for the same purposes.

Some croakers lack a swimbladder and, as if not wishing to be outdone by their relatives, they make a small amount of sound by grinding their teeth.

The Unsilent Sea

There was a time when we thought of the dark depths as being noiseless and talked of 'The Silent Sea'. With the development of underwater listening devices, this notion has been blown skyhigh. In addition to the croakers and the many other fishes now known to break the underwater silence, it has been discovered that whales, dolphins and porpoises are always chattering to each other or using sounds to test the depth of water beneath them, or to locate food. Even lowly shrimps and prawns add to the submarine cacophony.

There are other sounds to add to the confusion. A submarine in the First World War followed a supposed enemy submarine, only to find it was picking up the heartbeat of a large whale! In the Second World War, with more sophisticated listening devices, submarines, picking up the sounds of croakers and other fishes, suspected enemy craft were in the neighbourhood. Later they used the sound barrage to mask their own noises. It was wartime experiences of this kind that gave a stimulus to research on sound-producing fishes.

The sirens unmasked

Modern naval personnel were not the first to be deceived. It has been suggested that the song of the Sirens, the subject of the Greek myth, may have been nothing more than the 'voices' of the meagre or weakfish, which is common in the Mediterranean. This is a member of the croaker family which ranges from southern Australia to South Africa and the Mediterranean. Occasional individuals, up to 6 ft or more long, appear from time to time off the coasts of the British Isles.

vagus nerve — muscle — cavity — muscle — muscle — septum — air bladder — gas glands

◁ *The sound mechanics of a croaker's swimbladder, with the cutaway sections' plan views at far left. At a very rapid rate—about 24 contractions per second—the muscle surrounding the bladder cavities vibrates with much the same effect as the strings of a guitar, with the bladder cavities amplifying the sound.*

class	**Pisces**
order	**Perciformes**
family	**Sciaenidae**
genera & species	***Micropogon undulatus*** *Atlantic croaker*
	Roncador stearnsi *spotfin croaker*
	Sciaena aquila *meagre*
	Umbrina roncador *yellowfin croaker*
	others

Like an extra for a film on the first amphibious reptiles, a small saltwater crocodile comes ashore in Queensland, Australia. Unlike alligators, crocodiles can be found in brackish waters, estuaries, and swimming out at sea.

Crocodile

The crocodiles and their close relatives alligators, caimans and gharials are the sole survivors of the great group of reptiles, the Archosauria, that included the well-known and awe-inspiring dinosaurs. The crocodile family itself includes the dwarf crocodiles and the false gharial as well as the dozen or so species of true crocodiles.

Crocodiles are often distinguished by the shape of the snout. This is long and broad in the Nile crocodile, the best-known species, short in the Indian marsh crocodile or mugger, and long and narrow in the false gharial. The differences between crocodiles and alligators are set out under alligator, p 29.

As with many large, fearsome animals, the size of crocodiles has been exaggerated. There is reliable evidence for the Nile crocodile reaching 20 ft and American and Orinoco crocodiles have measured 23 ft. At the other extreme the Congo dwarf crocodile has never been found to exceed 3 ft 9 in. Now that crocodiles have been hunted too intensively, large ones have become extremely rare.

Cold-blooded lover of warmth

Crocodiles are found in the warmer parts of the world, in Africa, Asia, Australia and America. Unlike alligators, they are often found in brackish water and sometimes they even swim out to sea. Estuarine crocodiles swim between the islands of the Malay Archipelago and stray ones have been found in the Fijis and other remote islands.

Reptiles are said to be cold-blooded because they cannot maintain their body temperatures within fine limits, as can mammals and birds. A reptile's body temperature is usually within a few degrees of that of its surroundings. It cannot shiver to keep warm or sweat to keep cool. Many reptiles, however, can keep their body temperatures from varying too much by following a daily routine to avoid extremes of temperature. Crocodiles do this. They come out of the water at sunrise and lie on the banks basking in the sun. When their bodies have warmed up, they either move into the shade or back into the water, escaping the full strength of the midday sun. Then in the late afternoon they bask again, and return to the water by nightfall. By staying underwater at night they conserve heat, because water holds its heat better than air.

Stones in their stomachs

When crocodiles come out of the water they generally stay near the bank, although occasionally they wander some distance in search of water, and can cause great consternation by appearing in towns. They are generally sluggish, but, considering their bulky bodies and relatively short legs, they are capable of unexpected bursts of speed. They have three distinct gaits. There is a normal walk, with the body lifted well off the ground with the legs under the body—a gait most unlike the popular

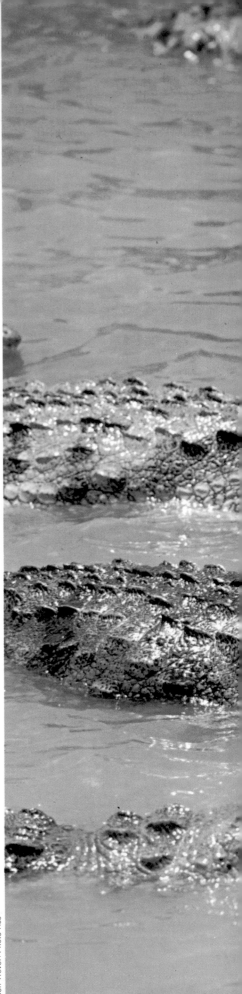

△ *A crocodile heads for the water in its normal walking gait: body well clear of the ground, with the legs striding stiffly beneath the body.*

▷ *The drifting menace—crocodiles in their classic lurking pose, motionless, awash, for all the world like drifting logs.*

△ *Young Nile crocodiles bask on a river bank whose soil is polished from the friction of crocodile bellies sliding towards the water.*

▽ *Crocodiles taking to water in a hurry slide over the edge of river banks on their bellies, using their legs as paddles.*

△ *Saltwater or estuarine crocodile: one of the world's most dangerous crocodiles, it can reach lengths of over 20 ft.*

▽ *Smaller relative, different jaw structure: the broad-fronted crocodile of West Africa only grows to 5—6 ft and does not attack man.*

conception of a crocodile walking. More familiar is the tobogganing used when dashing into the water. The crocodile slides on its belly, using its legs as paddles. The third method is used by a young crocodile which will occasionally gallop along with the front and back legs working together, like a bounding squirrel.

In the water, crocodiles float very low, with little more than eyes and nostrils showing. They habitually carry several pounds of stones in their stomachs, which help to stabilise their bodies. The stones lie in the stomach, below the centre of gravity and work as a counterpoise to the buoyant lungs. This is particularly useful when the crocodiles are fairly young. At that age they are top heavy and cannot float easily at the surface.

Maneaters: myth and fact

For the first year of their lives, young crocodiles feed on small animals, frogs, dragonflies, crabs and even mosquito larvae. Young crocodiles have been seen cornering the larvae by curving their bodies and tails around them. Larger animals are stalked. The baby crocodile swims stealthily towards its prey then pounces, snapping at it with a sideways movement of the jaws, necessary because the crocodile's eyes are at the side of its head.

As a crocodile grows the amount of insects in its diet falls, and it turns to eating snails and fish. The adult crocodiles continue to catch fish but turn increasingly to trapping mammals and birds. They capture their prey by lying in wait near game trails or waterholes. When a victim approaches the crocodile will seize it and drag it underwater or knock it over with a blow from its tail or head. Once the victim is pulled into the water the crocodile has a definite advantage. Drowning soon stills the victim's struggles, and, grasping a limb in its jaws, the crocodile may roll over and over so that the victim is dismembered.

Crocodiles are well-known as maneaters— but how true is this reputation? The maneating habit varies and it may be that only certain individuals will attack man. In parts of Africa, crocodiles are not regarded as a menace at all, while elsewhere palisades have to be erected at the water's edge to allow the women to fetch water in safety. It seems that crocodiles are likely to be more aggressive when their streams and pools dry up so they cannot escape, or when they are guarding their young.

In the crocodile's nest

The Nile crocodile breeds when 5—10 years old. By this time it is 7—10 ft long. The fullgrown males stake out their territories along the banks and share them with younger males and females. They defend the territories by fighting, which may sometimes end in one contestant being killed.

A male crocodile approaches a female crocodile and displays to her by thrashing the water with his snout and tail. They swim in circles with the male on the outside trying to get near her so he can put a forelimb over her body and mate.

Up to 90 eggs are laid during the dry season. They hatch 4 months·later, during the rainy season when there are plenty of insects about for the babies to feed on.

The Nile crocodile and the marsh crocodile dig pits 2 ft deep for their nests, but the estuarine crocodile of northern Australia and southeast Asia makes a mound of leaves. The nests are built near water and shade, where the female can guard her brood and keep herself cool. During the incubation period she stays by the nest defending it against enemies, including other crocodiles, although in colonies they sometimes nest only a few yards apart.

The baby crocodiles begin to grunt before hatching. This is the signal for the mother to uncover the nest. The babies climb out and stay near her, yapping if they get lost. They follow her about like ducklings and forage for insects, even climbing trees, and grunting and snapping at one another. They disperse after a few days.

The young Nile crocodiles are about 1 ft long at hatching and for their first 7 years they grow at a rate of about 10 in. a year.

Cannibals

The mother crocodile has to be on her guard all the time as many animals will wait for their chance to eat the eggs or the baby crocodiles. Their main enemy is the monitor lizard. They are bold enough to dig underneath the crocodile as she lies over her nest, and once a male monitor was seen to decoy a crocodile away from the nest while the female stole the eggs. Other crocodiles, herons, mongooses, turtles, eagles and predatory fish all eat baby crocodiles. Adult crocodiles have been killed by lions, elephants, and leopards, and hippopotamuses will attack crocodiles in defence of their young.

Crocodiles are cannibals, so basking groups are always sorted out into parties of equal size and the smaller crocodiles keep well away from the bigger ones.

Crocodile tears

If we say that someone is shedding crocodile tears it means that they are showing grief or sympathy that they do not really mean. The idea that crocodiles are hypocrites is an ancient one, and is described in TH White's translation of a 12th century bestiary: 'Crocodiles lie by night in the water, by day on land, because hypocrites, however luxuriously they live by night, delight to be said to live holily and justly by day.' The hypocrisy seems to be manifested in the form of tears, and malicious or misunderstanding comparisons are made with women's tears. Thus when Desdemona weeps, Othello complains:

'O devil, devil!
If that the earth could teem with woman's tears,
Each drop she falls would prove a crocodile.'

John Hawkins explains crocodile's tears as meaning 'that as the Crocodile when he crieth, goeth then about most to deceive, so doth a woman commonly when she weepeth'. The deception practised by the 'cruell craftie crocodile' is that it lures unwary travellers into drawing near to find out what is the matter.

The story, like many myths and legends, may have a basis of truth. It could have

△ *Hatching out: while still in the egg, baby Nile crocodiles grunt a signal to the mother to uncover the nest.*

▽ *Prelude to feeding: prey trapped in its vice-like jaws, a crocodile returns to the water where it will take its meal at leisure.*

sprung from the plaintive howling that crocodiles make. Crocodiles, however, do have tear glands to keep their eyes moist and tears, or water trapped in their lids, may run from the corners of their eyes. This, with the permanent grin of their jaws, could have led to their legendary reputation as hypocrites.

class	**Reptilia**
order	**Crocodilia**
family	**Crocodylidae**
genera & species	***Crocodylus niloticus*** *Nile crocodile*
	C. porosus *estuarine crocodile*
	C. palustris *marsh crocodile*
	Osteolaemus *dwarf crocodiles*
	Tomistoma schlegeli *false gharial*

▷ *'African crocodiles at home': a romanticized print shows waterfowl scattering in panic from the threat of an evil-looking flock of crocodiles. But, as the picture below shows, nearby birds are in no danger when crocodiles haul out onto the bank to bask with jaws agape. Birds can safely pick parasites from the skin of basking crocodiles, and have been seen to pick leeches and food fragments from crocodiles' teeth and tongues. The birds get away with this because basking crocodiles are not interested in hunting—even food in the mouth does not interest them. Indeed, crocodiles have a definite taste for cannibalism, and so basking groups are always made up of crocodiles of equal size. Smaller crocodiles take care to keep well away from the bigger ones.*

Mansell

Photo Library Inc

558

Crossbill

Crossbills are parrot-like finches with unmistakable bills in which the upper and lower mandibles cross over, as if deformed. The male crossbill has brick-red or carmine plumage with blackish wings and tail. The females are yellowish or olive and are easily confused with greenfinches. The two-barred crossbill has distinctive white bars on its wings.

The common or red crossbill breeds around the world in the northern hemisphere, from Newfoundland to Alaska in North America and from Scotland to Japan in the Old World. It ranges as far south as Nicaragua, the Philippines and Annam, in southeast Asia, wherever there are coniferous forests. Throughout their range, crossbills breed only where there are coniferous trees, so there are isolated populations in many places; in Spain among the localised areas of Scots firs and Mediterranean pines, and in Algeria, where there are Aleppo pines.

The very similar parrot crossbill is found in pine forests of Scandinavia, the Baltic states and northern Russia. The two-barred crossbill lives in Canada, Siberia and northern Russia. It has also become established in the mountain pine forests of Hispaniola, in the West Indies.

Crossbill irruptions

Crossbills are subject to marked fluctuations and invading armies of these attractive small birds move across the country. Because crossbills are dependent on pine, spruce and larch cones for food they have to move about in search of suitable supplies, and the size of crossbill populations varies from year to year, depending on the quality of cone crops. Usually the crossbills do not move far, but every few years they irrupt — that is, there is a large-scale exodus from the traditional breeding grounds into countries where they are not normally found. The irruptions occur when a small crop of cones follows a good one. In the first year the crossbills flourish and most of their young survive the first winter to breed and increase the population in the spring. In the next year there is a shortage of food for this large population, and, as has happened in human affairs, some have to leave to seek a home in empty lands.

Occasionally there are crossbill irruptions into the British Isles, when large numbers of crossbills, sometimes including some parrot crossbills, cross the North Sea from Scandinavia. Meteorological records show that this happens when there are northeasterly winds blowing from Norway to Britain at the time of the crossbills' movement.

After an irruption, immigrant crossbills breed in the British Isles, especially southeast England, but die out within a few years.

Seed splitters

The main food of crossbills is the seed from cones of pines, larch, spruce and other conifers. They occasionally eat other seeds such as apple, hawthorn, thrift, crowberry and oats, when cones are in short supply — for instance during their irruptions, when they land in places like the Shetlands where there are very few trees. Some insects, especially those living in galls, are also eaten.

Seeds are taken from the cones while they are still on the tree, the crossbills climbing on to the cones, often using their bills as an extra support, like a parrot does. Fallen cones are eaten usually only towards the end of winter or in spring when food is running short. The crossed bill is used to wrench off the scales and split them vertically, while the seed is dextrously extracted with the tongue.

Diet depends on bill size

The crossbills that appear in the British Isles have been found to feed on different seeds in spring and autumn. Pine seeds are eaten more than larch in the spring, probably because pine cones take 2 years to ripen and the crossbills can open them easily only when they are ripe. Larch and spruce cones are softer. They take only 1 year to ripen and the crossbills can deal with them at any time.

The ability of these crossbills to open one kind of cone and not another depends on the strength and size of the bill, and it has been found that different crossbills prefer different cones. Size of the bill and the toughness of the preferred cone are related. The common crossbill, as we have seen, is best able to deal with spruce and larch, whereas the heavier billed parrot crossbill feeds mainly on the harder pine cones. The two-barred crossbill, with a small bill, lives on the small soft cones of larch. The Scottish crossbill has a heavier bill than the common crossbill. This is one of the main reasons why the Scottish crossbills are thought to be parrot crossbills rather than common crossbills.

Straight-billed chicks

Nests are built in trees on the edge of woodland or beside rides and clearings, never in dense forest. Thin twigs, moss, grass and other materials are made into an untidy nest by the female. The male accompanies her on collecting trips, although he very rarely carries any material. The twigs are used as a foundation in a fork near the trunk, or far out among the evergreen foliage.

The clutch usually consists of 4 eggs which are incubated by the female alone for 12 – 13 days. During this time the male brings food to her, and she does not leave the nest. Apparently she calls when hungry and the male flies from his perch near the nest to search for food.

The newly-hatched chicks are very resistant to cold, as well they need to be, for the female may leave them for an hour or more in the cold weather of a Scandinavian or Canadian spring. When they are about a week old, the chicks can control their body temperature, but before this they chill off and become almost lifeless when exposed. They recover in a few minutes when the female broods them. It is a form of temporary hibernation such as has been more fully studied in swift nestlings. .

Crossbill fledgelings have normal, straight bills which grow askew when the birds leave the nest.

Until the chicks begin to open their eyes, the male feeds the female, who passes on the food to the chicks. Now he starts to feed them himself. By weighing chicks before and after their meals a Swedish ornithologist calculated that a crossbill chick receives about 3 500 seeds a day. With four or more chicks in a clutch this is a measure of how busy the parents must be kept, extracting seeds from cones.

When they hatch, the young crossbills have ordinary bills with the mandibles meeting at the tip. It is not until after they leave the nest that the two halves cross over by growing crooked. The upper mandible may cross either to left or right of the lower.

Classification problem

In the pine forests of northern Scotland there is a resident population of crossbills, the only one in the British Isles. Ornithologists have disagreed as to which species these belong. The authoritative *Handbook of British Birds*, published in 1940, classes the Scottish crossbill as a race of the common crossbill, but more recently it has been regarded by others as an isolated population of the parrot crossbill. This view is not, however, held by everyone. Some ornithologists think that the common and parrot crossbills belong to the same species, which partly solves the problem.

class	**Aves**
order	**Passeriformes**
family	**Fringillidae**
genus & species	*Loxia curvirostris* common crossbill
	L. pityopsittacus *parrot crossbill*
	L. leucoptera *two-barred crossbill*

Heavy of bill,
bold and aggressive
— the American crow

Crow

The crow family, including about 100 species, contains some of the best known and engaging of the perching birds. Many of them, such as the raven, rook, magpie and jay, we shall meet again under their separate headings. Here we are concerned with the carrion crow, which originally gave the name to the family. Mention will also be made of other species similar to it, such as the common crow and fish crow of North America. The hooded crow of Europe and Asia is now regarded as belonging to the same species as the carrion crow, the two being separate subspecies.

The carrion crow, 19 in. long, appears black all over, even at a short distance. Close to, its plumage is shot with blue and purple, especially in strong sunlight. The common American crow is similar in size, appearance and habits except that it gathers to sleep in roosts several thousand strong. The fish crow is slightly smaller, and frequents coastal flats and rivers, feeding largely on shellfish. The hooded crow has similar habits to the carrion crow but is distinguished from it by its grey mantle and underparts. Where the ranges of these two crows overlap they readily interbreed.

Pamela Harrison

A carrion crow soaring. Crows are powerful fliers and are noted for their slow, deliberate wing-beat; but like rooks they will often indulge in noisy, striking aerobatic displays.

Crow versus rook

The carrion crow's day is spent mainly on the ground feeding or perched in trees, often solitary or in pairs, sometimes in parties or flocks of not more than a couple of dozen. Sometimes crows will associate with flocks of rooks, but the old saying about the large black birds in Britain, that if there are one or two on their own they are crows, if in a flock they are rooks, is generally correct.

At close quarters a rook can be distinguished by the grey skin at the base of the beak, the carrion crow by the black feathers on the base of the bill, although first-year rooks also have this. There are a number of minor ways of telling a crow from a rook at a distance, but even experienced field naturalists confess occasional doubt. One infallible way is to watch the actions of the bird when cawing. A crow throws its head up and brings it down again as it caws, at the same time depressing and fanning the tail. A rook lowers its head as it calls, so beak, neck and body are more or less horizontal. At the same time the tail is held up in a fan.

The flight of a crow is slow and deliberate with regular wing-beats.

Crows use communal roosts in autumn and winter, sharing at times the rooks' roosts, but even where many European crows gather to sleep in groups of trees they number less than roosts of American crows.

No food wasted

Their food is very varied. Plant food includes seeds, grass, fruits such as cherry and apple, root crops, acorns and walnuts. Animal food ranges from insects, especially beetles, and their larvae, frogs, toads, small birds and eggs, to small mammals and carrion. Injured or sick animals, birds or small mammals are killed. On the shore, shellfish such as mussels and winkles are taken, and in streams swan mussels are eaten.

Crow courtship

The male crow courts by bowing with the fanned tail moving up and down in time with the head. The nest is typically in a stout fork of a tree, where main branches come away, but it may be in a bush or on a cliff. It is built in April mainly, if not entirely, by the male, of sticks with some earth and moss and a lining of grass, hair or wool. The 4—5 eggs, exceptionally as many as 7, pale blue to light green, are incubated by the female, who is fed on the nest by the male. They hatch in 19—20 days, the nestlings being fed at first by the hen and later by both parents, who bring food in their throat-pouch. This lasts for 30—35 days.

Few enemies

The beak of a crow is strong and powerful, and the bird probably has few regular enemies. Two crows are more than a match for a hawk or a fox, but one on its own, especially a sick or aged bird, could fall victim. In captivity, crows live 12 or more years, and probably do so in the wild. Little study has been made of causes of death among juveniles, but the death-rate is probably as high as in those species of birds in which it has been studied: that is, 60—70% in the first 3—6 months.

Punch-drunk crow

Birds often tap at windows. The usual explanation is that the male, occupying a territory in which there is a window, sees his image in the glass and attacks it, as he would a rival. In some instances, the male will spend so much time during the breeding season attacking his own reflection that his behaviour seems to amount to a mania. An extreme example was recorded in 1960 of a

John Markham

◁ *Coloured variant: the hooded crow. The various races replace each other geographically and hooded and carrion crows interbreed freely where their ranges overlap. Especially in northern Europe, huge flocks of hooded crows, migrating by daylight, present a striking sight.*

▷ *Scavengers meet: pied crows and hooded vultures gather for siesta on a golf course in Ghana.*

▽ *The bulky, no-nonsense bill of the carrion crow. The bird's nostrils are at the base of the bill, shielded by the forward-facing bristles.*

▽▷ *A trio of hungry optimists: carrion crow chicks. Nestling crows are fed first by the hen and later by both parents for 30—35 days.*

Roy A Harris and KR Duff

Jane Burton: Photo Res

AW Puchalski: Photo Res

△ *Three angry hooded crows make a pass at a buzzard. Agile in the air and aggressive to potential enemies, all crows mob birds of prey.*

▽ *The carrion crow's day is spent mainly on the ground or feeding in trees. They seldom congregate in large flocks, as rooks will do.*

crow that can be described only as punch-drunk.

In June, 1960, at the home of Mr Peter Thomas, at Virginia Water, a few miles from the outskirts of London, a male crow started attacking the windows. The attacks went on for about a week then petered out. Each morning soon after dawn the crow appeared before the French windows and began flying at them. His hen accompanied him but took no part in the attacks.

During the day a pane of glass 5½ ft high by 1 ft 7 in. wide became so spattered with blood at the end of the attack that it was difficult to put a finger between the stains. There was also mud from the bird's feet, smears of saliva, and some food from the crow's throat-pouch.

Another pane was soiled in the same way, but in only the upper half, and a third and fourth were similarly soiled over the top foot or so.

Each evening Mr Thomas thoroughly cleaned the windows. He also put up a barricade made of a pair of step-ladders at each side, with planks from one to the other, and on the planks were placed as many boxes, empty oil-drums and other obstacles as he could muster. Despite these obstructions the crow still got through to batter himself repeatedly.

The attacks were ritualized. At about 7 ft from the window was a bank 2 ft high. The crow always took off from this bank and from the same spot. After flying at the window and banging hard at it with his beak he fluttered to the ground, returned to the bank, strutted up and down in front of the hen, cawing, then made for the identical spot to take off for another attack.

The loss of blood seemed not to affect the bird.

By a strange coincidence, that same year another crow behaved in almost the same way at a house several miles away. The owner of that house, unnerved by being wakened every morning by the repeated banging on the window, bought a gun and shot the crow. In a few days another crow arrived and started the same performance. It also was shot. A few days later another turned up to continue the attacks. By now the breeding season of the carrion crow was waning, and in a few days the attacks by the third crow petered out, so this bird was not shot.

The only possible explanation of this behaviour can be that it is linked with the breeding season, and is touched off by the crows seeing their reflections in windows. More difficult to explain is the persistence in spite of what must have been considerable loss of blood. The only comparison seems to be with a punch-drunk boxer, who seems to want to be hurt.

class	**Aves**
order	**Passeriformes**
family	**Corvidae**
genus & species	***Corvus albus*** *pied crow* ***C. corone*** *carrion crow* ***C. cornix*** *hooded crow* ***C. brachyrhynchos*** *American crow* ***C. oxifragus*** *fish crow* *others*

Crowned eagle

The crowned eagle is the most powerful African eagle and although it is not as large as the martial eagle it takes the heaviest prey. It measures 27–30 in. long, has a bluish-grey bill and yellow feet and the legs are feathered right down to the toes. The crowned eagle gets its name from the crest that rises from the crown of its head. The crest feathers are black and white, the head and neck olive-grey. The upper parts are black with a bluish, plum-like bloom, except for edgings of white and grey on the tail coverts. The underparts are white, barred and spotted with white.

The crowned eagle has the broad rounded wings and long tail typical of eagles living in dense forests. It is found in the southern half of Africa from Ghana to the Sudan and south to the Cape Province of South Africa. The habitat ranges from heavy rain forests to open savannah and crowned eagles are not found in the arid areas of Southern or Eastern Africa.

More common than supposed

The crowned eagle has been considered rare even by comparison with other eagles, which never have dense populations because each pair needs a large range in which to hunt. In fact crowned eagles are more common than was supposed. Previously they had been overlooked because they fly just above or within the canopy of the trees when hunting, and, unlike other large eagles, perch within dense foliage rather than on a bare branch or rocky crag where they could command a good view over the country. The nests are also difficult to find, frequently being hidden among trees at a considerable height. Often the only way to find a nest is to listen for the loud calls of the young as the parents fly in with food.

Mammal-hunters

The nests, and the ground below, are liberally scattered with the bones of the crowned eagles' prey. They are nearly all of mammals; only a few bird remains have been found and only occasionally are reptiles killed. The largest animals taken by crowned eagles are antelopes such as the forest dwelling suni and nearly full-grown duikers, but the usual prey are monkeys such as the colobus and vervet, hyraxes, mongooses and other mammals of a similar size.

The toll taken of monkeys has probably been exaggerated and it seems incorrect to call the crowned eagle a monkey-eating eagle, as has been done. In some places the eagles appear to take very few monkeys, although the monkeys certainly react with cries when an eagle comes into sight. It seems likely that a monkey can be caught only by surprise as the eagle swoops over the canopy. Colobus monkeys may be particularly vulnerable as they sun themselves in the morning and evening. Surprise is necessary as monkeys will defend themselves vigorously if attacked and a colobus monkey has been seen keeping a crowned eagle at bay. To avoid the monkey's retaliation, a crowned eagle is reported to swoop past, grabbing the monkey by the head then dropping it so that it falls to the ground. The eagle then dives and kills it before it can recover.

Breeding every other year

Crowned eagle nests are found high up in trees, perhaps as much as 80 ft. In open country they can easily be seen from the ground but in forests they are hidden in foliage. The most usual nest sites are large trees by a stream or on the steep side of a valley. The nest is used from year to year, and one in South Africa is known to have been in use for at least 75 years. Each year more material is added and the structure becomes enormous. Most of the material consists of branches complete with foliage ripped from the tree. The male collects most of the material while the female works it into the nest.

Courtship displays, as in other birds of prey, take the form of aerial games. The eagles fly up and down as if on a switchback, flapping their wings just enough to gain height on a soar before plunging down again. The display may carry them to great heights, where they are invisible to the naked eye. One observer calculated that a pair of crowned eagles were displaying at 5 000 ft.

Incubation of the 2 eggs lasts 6 or 7 weeks. The female does most of the incubating, while the male brings her food. The chicks spend up to 4 months on the nest before flying, and during this time the elder chick apparently kills the younger. At least, in the rather small number of nests studied, only one chick has ever survived and it is presumed that the other is killed by its nest mate.

After starting to fly, the young eagle returns to the nest to be fed. It does not stray far and returns hurriedly whenever it sees a parent arriving with food. Later it wanders farther afield, learning to hunt for itself, but continues to be fed by the parent for a year after leaving the nest, after which it loses interest in its parents. Because of the long breeding cycle, 17–18 months from repairing the nest to the independence of the young, crowned eagles can breed only every other year.

Enemies

High in the trees, crowned eagle nests are usually safe from enemies, and smaller birds of prey sometimes nest near them, apparently obtaining protection from their larger neighbours. Baboons have robbed nests of crowned eagles, however.

In West Africa, crowned eagles are hunted for their feathers. Some tribes permit them to be worn only by chiefs and their relatives.

Below and overleaf: The majestic, unmistakable head of the crowned eagle, beautiful heavyweight of the eagles of Africa. It is never found in dense populations because each pair needs a wide range in which to hunt, and for this reason the crowned eagle has always been considered rare—incorrectly—compared with other eagles.

Phillip Wayre: NHPA

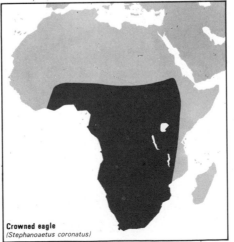

Crowned eagle
(Stephanoaetus coronatus)

Eking out their food

The long adolescence that prevents the adults breeding more than once in two years is not common even among large birds. The harpy eagle breeds every other year, and so do the wandering albatrosses and king penguins. The latter two are faced with this necessity because of the difficulty in obtaining enough food for the large young during the long Antarctic winter. The slow breeding rate of the crowned and harpy eagles is, probably, also related to food supply, but for a different reason. Both eagles feed on large mammals such as monkeys and antelopes that, themselves, have a slow rate of reproduction. So it helps the eagles not to kill too many prey animals in a short time, as would happen if they raised young every year. Instead, they raise a small number of young but these are well-fed and have a very good chance of survival. Other large eagles, such as the golden eagle, breed every year, but their prey is rabbits and hares that have large litters making up quickly for the losses due to eagles.

The early death of the younger of the two chicks in a brood is also probably part of the same story. The parents would have difficulty in getting sufficient food for both.

class	**Aves**
order	**Falconiformes**
family	**Accipitridae**
genus & species	***Stephanoaetus coronatus***

Cuckoo

The cuckoo is regarded in sharply contrasting ways; it is to some the harbinger of spring, to others, a base parasite. Of the many species, only the common cuckoo of Europe and Asia gives the loud insistent call that has given rise to the name. It is called **coucou** in French, **Kuckuck** in German, **Kukushka** in Russian and **Kak-ko** in Japanese.

The common cuckoo has distinctive black and white barring on the underparts and a grey head and neck. The tail is long and the wings narrow, so in flight the cuckoo looks very much like a hawk. It can be distinguished, however, by its longer neck, the shape of the head and a pale streak under the wing.

Other cuckoos are gaudy by comparison with the common cuckoo. The red-winged Indian cuckoo has a magpie-like tail and a black head, back and tail. Related to it is the great spotted cuckoo, similar in shape but with white spots on the wings and back. The emerald cuckoo of South Africa is a brilliant golden green, except for a yellow belly.

Cuckoos belong to two subfamilies, with their relatives the anis, roadrunners, couas and coucals in other subfamilies. One subfamily, to which the common cuckoo belongs, ranges across the Old World from western Europe to Polynesia, while the other belongs to both Old and New Worlds. The former are all parasitic; the female lays her eggs in other birds' nests. It is for this habit that the cuckoos are best known, but it is by no means widespread in the family as a whole (see Ani p 56 and Coucal p 538).

Long migrations
Many cuckoos migrate over thousands of miles, from the tropics to the temperate regions. The common cuckoos begin to arrive in the British Isles in the last few days of March and leave during July to early September, each bird flying on its own bound for tropical Africa although exactly where is not known. The shining cuckoo of New Zealand makes an even more impressive migration, across 2 000 miles of ocean to the Solomon Islands. How they find their way over vast distances is especially puzzling as the young birds migrate from the breeding grounds several weeks after the adults have gone. This is sure proof that the urge to migrate, the ability to navigate, and the knowledge of the route are inherited, for there is absolutely no chance of the young cuckoos learning from their elders.

Feeds on many pests
Cuckoos eat insects, especially the larvae, but they will also eat worms, spiders, and centipedes. The beetles, flies, dragonflies, butterflies and moths eaten often include those harmful to agriculture; for instance, cockchafers, cabbage white butterflies and wireworms. In particular they eat hairy or

The lodger awaits acceptance in hedge sparrow's nest. When the foster parent is away the cuckoo flies down, lifts an egg out, swallows it or drops it and lays one of her own in its place.

toxic caterpillars including those of the cinnabar moth which are usually left alone by other birds. The yellow-billed and black-billed cuckoos of North America are useful because they eat the tent caterpillars that weave large communal shelters, from which they sally forth to strip trees of their leaves. Fruit is sometimes eaten, especially by the koel, a cuckoo of Asia and Australia.

Boarding out the children
It has been well-known since ancient times that the common cuckoo does not build a nest of its own, but lays its eggs in those of other birds. Other members of the cuckoo family do the same, as do other kinds of birds; for example, the cowbird and the honeyguide. It is far from easy to watch the cuckoo lay an egg in the host nest as so much depends on being in the right place at the right time. Nevertheless, the amazing ways in which she ensures that her offspring have a good chance of surviving until independent are now well-known.

The female cuckoo keeps a watch for small birds building their nests. When the nest is complete and the unwitting foster parent has laid an egg, the cuckoo flies down. Choosing a time when the foster parent is away, she lifts an egg out of the nest, swallows or drops it, and very quickly lays one of her own in its place and departs before the foster parent returns.

Cuckoo eggs are sometimes found in domed nests of willow warblers and it was once thought that the cuckoo laid her egg on the ground then carried it to the nest in her bill, but it is now known that she

presses her body against the nest and ejects the egg through the entrance. In Australia and New Zealand the shining cuckoo lays in domed nests of wrens by forcing its head in through the entrance then out through the far wall. The egg is laid while it straddles the nest, then it scrambles out through the hole it has made. The foster parent, when it returns, merely repairs the gap in the nest.

Observations have shown that clutches with a cuckoo egg are more likely to be deserted than normal clutches, but usually the cuckoo egg is accepted. It hatches in 12½ days and often the chick emerges before its nestmates. This advantage is used by the baby cuckoo to evict the other eggs and any newly hatched young. It is perhaps this part of the parasitic habit, more than any other, that has earned the cuckoo its bad name. The baby cuckoo manoeuvres itself in the bottom of the nest so that an egg or chick becomes balanced on its back, between the wings. It then hoists the unfortunate creature out of the nest, to be followed by the others. Occasionally two cuckoo eggs may be laid in one nest, when two female cuckoos are keeping watch in one area. After a few days jostling, the urge to empty the nest of competitors dies away and both young cuckoos grow together.

If the cuckoo did not evict its nestmates they would surely die in any case, for the young cuckoo grows rapidly, and its foster parents are hard put to feed it. After 3 weeks it leaves the nest which it has outgrown, and the foster parents keep feeding it, often having to perch on its back to drop insects in the gaping beak.

The African emerald cuckoo is a brilliant golden green except for its yellow belly.

Almost ready to moult at the end of the season, hedge sparrow feeds its giant foster child.

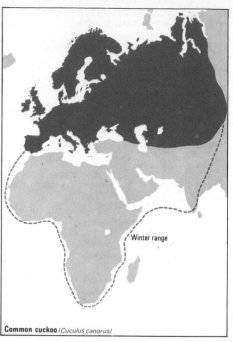

Winter range

Common cuckoo (Cuculus canorus)

The common cuckoo arrives in Britain in late March leaving between July and September.

The baby cuckoo usually hatches first and begins to evict the other eggs.

The second egg does not survive long, being ejected from the nest in the same manner.

A newly-hatched tree pipit receives the same treatment being unable to defend itself.

Matching egg colours

Surveys of clutches containing cuckoo eggs show that the cuckoo egg is often very similar to the foster parents' eggs, and it has also been found that in any area cuckoos use certain host nests more than others. In Hungary, the chief dupe of the common cuckoo is the great reed warbler, and the cuckoo lays greenish eggs blotched with brown and black, like those of the warbler. In Finland, cuckoos' eggs are blue like those of its hosts the whinchat and redstart. Nearly all over its range, there are these preferences for certain hosts with a mimicking of their eggs. It seems that this reduces the chance of the foster parent abandoning the nest.

In the British Isles, however, cuckoo eggs differ surprisingly from their hosts'—yet they all tend to be of one pattern. The explanation for this seems to be that a cuckoo may lay in nests of another host if it cannot find the right one, and in Britain, where the countryside is divided into many small habitats with a large variety of possible host species, the cuckoo has not been able to form any set preferences.

The final deception

Before the mysteries of bird migration were revealed it was thought the cuckoos turned into sparrowhawks in the winter and, even now, it is not unusual for a cuckoo to be mistaken for a sparrowhawk because of the similarity of shape and plumage. Bird watchers are not the only ones to be deceived as, when the cuckoo returns in spring, small birds will gather to mob it as if it were a hawk. There is some evidence that the cuckoos make use of this mistake. Cuckoos have been seen flying in an even more hawk-like fashion than usual, flapping and gliding in a soaring flight very much like a bird of prey. When they settle they are sometimes mobbed by meadow pipits and other small birds. On a few occasions this behaviour has been followed by the cuckoo alighting near a meadow pipit's nest, and one was seen flying away with a pipit's egg which it swallowed. It seems then that the cuckoo indulges in this hawk-like flight just before egg-laying, to lure the owners of the nest away by false pretences so that it can sneak in and lay its own egg.

Evidence for this is not conclusive but similar behaviour has been seen in other cuckoos. An Indian hawk-cuckoo that imitates sparrowhawks has been seen to lure birds from their nests in a more positive fashion, and the koel mimics a crow which is its main host in India. The male koel is black and it flies up to the host nest, calling, and is promptly chased away by the crows. Apparently they do this not so much to ward off a parasitic bird but for the same reason of ownership for which they would drive away another crow. Meanwhile the brown female koel slips in to lay her egg. The baby koel, moreover, does not eject its nestmates but it looks so like a young crow that it is hardly distinguishable from its fellow nestlings.

Of all the parasitic birds, however, the cuckoos, by reducing egg size and incubation time, and by mimicry of host birds' eggs, have applied the greatest resource to their underhand art.

class	**Aves**
order	**Cuculiformes**
family	**Cuculidae**
genera & species	***Cuculus canorus*** *common cuckoo* ***C. varius*** *hawk-cuckoo* ***Clamator coromandus*** *red-winged Indian cuckoo* ***C. glandarius*** *greater spotted cuckoo* ***Chrysococcyx cupreus*** *emerald cuckoo* ***Chalcites lucidus*** *shining cuckoo* ***Coccyzus erythrophthalmus*** *black-billed cuckoo* ***C. americanus*** *yellow-billed cuckoo* ***Eudynamys scolopacea*** *koel others*

Cuckoo-shrike

Although the cuckoo-shrikes look like both cuckoos and shrikes, they are related to neither. Many of them have a shrike-like hooked bill and cuckoo-like black and white barred plumage on their underparts. In general the plumage is a dull combination of grey, black and white. The red-shouldered cuckoo-shrike does have a patch of red on each wing but is otherwise black. The barred cuckoo-shrike is very much like a common cuckoo, with a grey head and neck as well as a barred breast. The 14in. ground cuckoo-shrike is similar, and many cuckoo-shrikes have a cuckoo-like flight. The plumage of the sexes differs in all species, the females having a paler, less conspicuous colouring.

Some of the cuckoo-shrikes are commonly called greybirds, trillers, cicada birds or flycatcher shrikes. The minivets are in the cuckoo-shrike family but are distinct from the rest and are sometimes placed in a separate subfamily. They will be treated under a separate heading.

Cuckoo-shrikes live in Africa, the warmer parts of Asia through Malaya to New Guinea, Australia and the Solomon Islands.

Mixed parties

Some cuckoo-shrikes migrate, especially in Australia, moving from the south of the continent to the warmer northern parts in winter. The black-faced cuckoo-shrike occasionally strays to New Zealand. In Australia it is also known as the bluejay or shufflewing, the latter on account of the way it shuffles and restows its wings each time it alights.

Outside the breeding season cuckoo-shrikes live in flocks, often mixed with other birds. The black and white triller of the Philippines, for instance, is found with woodpeckers and orioles. Nearly all the cuckoo-shrikes live among trees, rarely coming down to the ground. One exception is the ground cuckoo-shrike of Australia which, outside the breeding season, lives in flocks on treeless plains. They are good runners, unlike other cuckoo-shrikes. Each flock is made up of a family, parents and offspring, that stays together from the time the chicks leave the nest until the next breeding season.

Caterpillar eaters

The scientific family name Campephagidae is more appropriate than cuckoo-shrike. It means 'caterpillar-eaters' and some cuckoo-shrikes, such as the white-winged triller, are helpful because they eat caterpillars that damage crops. Sometimes these cuckoo-shrikes are called caterpillar-shrikes, and another group are called cicada birds because of the large numbers of cicadas they eat. Cuckoo-shrikes eat a wide variety of other insects, however, including grasshoppers, bugs, beetles and spiders.

Some of the smaller species, such as the pigmy triller or pied shrike, hunt like flycatchers, flying out from a perch and returning after catching flying ants or other insects on the wing. Others hunt insects

New Guinea giant cuckoo-shrike feeding a small lizard to its snow-white nestling.

living on leaves and twigs, but the pied triller of Malaysia and the black-faced cuckoo-shrike of Australia sometimes take insects from the ground. The latter behaves like a shrike, watching from a favourite perch then swooping down to catch an insect or worm.

Frail nests

The nests of cuckoo-shrikes are built well up trees. Even the ground cuckoo-shrike builds in a fork 30 ft or so high. Made of grasses, flower stems, creepers and other soft vegetation bound together with cobwebs, the nest is small and fragile compared with the bird that sits in it. The nest of the white-winged triller is built with a rim 1 in. high but it is gradually flattened by the parents landing on it, until by the end of the season there is no more than a flat platform. The male alone builds the nest, and having done this and taken his share of the incubation, he feeds the chicks during their first week. After this he spends most of his time singing.

Attentive male

The male African white-breasted cuckoo-shrike also builds the nest on his own. He gathers only one tiny piece of material, perhaps a fine twig or blade of grass, on each collecting trip. One that was watched building his nest took 4 minutes on average to collect a piece of material and add it to the nest, and the nest took 6 days to complete. His mate played the part of overseer, doing no work except to test each piece of material as it was fastened in place.

In other species both sexes build the nest and incubate the eggs, or stand over them with wings half-opened to protect them from the sun. The ground cuckoo-shrike family stays together for the rest of the year, and before the families leave the breeding grounds, where the nests are close to each other, the young birds are fed indiscriminately by any adults, not necessarily their own parents.

Temperamental nesters

The male white-breasted cuckoo-shrike that was watched as it laboriously built its nest displayed an odd quirk of behaviour at the end of the breeding season. After the chick had left, the male destroyed the nest, tearing away the carefully laid materials and

dropping them around. This is a most unusual, and seemingly pointless, piece of behaviour. The only explanation that can be put forward—and it is dangerous to try to explain an action seen only once—is that it was a displacement activity. Displacement activities are thought to be the result of conflicting emotions which, because they cannot be settled by normal behaviour, are released by a piece of irrelevant behaviour. An example taken from the bird world is seen when a bird meets another at the boundary of its territory. It is not aggressive enough to attack, and not fearful enough to flee. Instead it does something irrelevant to the situation, such as preening. A similar human example is head scratching when confronted with a difficult problem. The proper context of head scratching is to relieve an itch, but here it is being used to relieve tension.

This is not the only occasion that a member of the cuckoo-shrike family has been seen to destroy its nest. In the event of disturbance, the shy black-faced cuckoo-shrike has been seen to take its nest apart, carry the material to another site and rebuild it. This is most unusual bird behaviour, since the patterns of nest building tend to follow in sequence, each one triggered by the end of the one before. Normally, as the nest nears completion, so the urge to have anything to do with further building fades.

class	**Aves**
order	**Passeriformes**
family	**Campephagidae**
genera & species	**Campephaga phoenicea** *red-shouldered cuckoo-shrike* **Coracina lineata** *barred cuckoo-shrike* **C. novae-hollandiae** *black-faced cuckoo-shrike* **C. pectoralis** *white-breasted cuckoo-shrike* **Pteropodocys maxima** *ground cuckoo-shrike* **Lalage melanoleuca** *black and white triller* **L. sueurii** *white-winged triller* **L. nigra** *pied triller* *others*

Red-wattled curassow. The curassows usually stay in trees, in forest or at its edge. They run with great agility along the branches, jumping up and up until they reach the tree-top, from where they take off, half gliding, half fluttering on short, rounded wings.

Curassow

There are 12 kinds of curassow, belonging to the same order as chickens, pheasants and quails. They range in size from a pheasant to a small turkey, the largest being the great curassow, which weighs $10\frac{1}{2}$ lb. The male's plumage is usually dark brown or black, sometimes relieved with white and glossed with dark green. The females of some species are similar to the males, others are more brown. Curassows have long tails and long legs and their most distinctive features are usually crests and horny casques, or helmets. The name is derived from the island of Curaçao, in the West Indies, although curassows have never lived there. In fact, curassows are restricted to the American mainland, from Mexico to Northern Argentina and Uruguay.

Birds with helmets

The curassows are unusual birds of the forests of Central and South America, which wear a variety of remarkable crests and casques, like the helmets of Roman soldiers. The crests are formed by a double row of short, stiff feathers. Some curl over the crown, as in the conspicuous white crest of the crested curassow. Others curl forwards as if 'permanently waved' as in the great and black curassows. The casques are bony, horn-covered projections rising from the top of the bill. That of the razor-billed curassow is orange-red and that of the helmeted curassow blue, 1–3 in. high, covering the crown of the head. Those curassows without a crest generally have wattles or a fleshy knob of red or yellow at the base of the bill, which swells and brightens in the breeding season.

They are found deep in forests or on the forest edges, and some come out into brush country. The species that live in the tall trees of the old forests are becoming rare as these trees are being destroyed.

Unlike their gamebird relatives, curassows spend much of their time in trees, although some live on the ground. The great curassow runs about the forest floor like a turkey but if frightened—it is very shy—it clambers through the undergrowth and up trees, half flying and half hopping until it can launch itself from a tree top and glide away to safety on short, rounded wings.

Feeding in the trees

Curassows feed on fruits, nuts, buds and young leaves and occasionally take insects and small frogs. The young seem to prefer insects. Apart from the ground-living great curassow, they feed mainly in the trees, only occasionally coming to the ground to feed on fallen fruit or to scratch through the litter on the forest floor, in a similar manner to a chicken.

Young fliers

Curassows are the only members of their order of gamebirds that nest in trees; the others rear their young on the ground. At the beginning of the breeding season male curassows take up territories and show off to rival males and prospective mates by calling from the tops of trees. Curassows have the trachea in their necks extended so it acts as an amplifier and their muffled-sounding bellows can be heard for some distance across the forest. Having attracted a female, the male curassow courts her by strutting up and down with tail raised and head held high, but the breast is tilted low and wings droop to display the white feathers under them.

The sharing of parental duties varies between species. The male great curassow builds the nest by himself but his mate feeds the chicks alone. Other curassows share the nest building, incubation of the eggs and the feeding of the chicks.

The nest is built of twigs and lined with green leaves, which are sometimes replaced when they dry out. It is small compared with the size of the curassow and so loosely woven that it is possible to see the 2 or 3 large, rough-shelled eggs from underneath. Incubation lasts about a month and the young hatch with their wing feathers already well-developed. They leave the nest and walk among the branches on their first day. Within 4 or 5 days they can fly confidently, but the young of the great

A shaggy, curling crest is found in several curassow species. The crested curassow is identified by the shape of its crest and yellow beak. This develops a yellow knob in adult males.

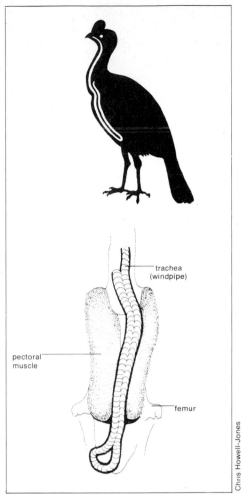

The curassow's trachea is extended down its breast so it acts as an amplifier of sound.

curassow, according to some accounts, throw themselves from the nest to the ground before they can fly. At first the chicks are fed mainly on insects by their parents, but soon learn to forage for themselves. Altogether this is an interesting combination of the characters of ground-nesting gamebirds and true tree nesters. The family often stays together for the rest of the year. Groups of curassows larger than one family are usually seen only where they have congregated around a plentiful crop of fruit.

Enemies

Living in the trees, curassows fall prey to tree-living carnivores such as kinkajous and jaguars, but the real threat to their existence is the same as that to bustards (p 331). Both birds are plump-bodied and delicious, curassow meat being like turkey but richer and more flavoured. Even if they were tasteless, the amount of meat on curassows would make them a favourite target in a part of the world that is both overpopulated and underfed.

Curassow for Christmas?

Europeans first saw curassows picking their way about villages in Central and South America, where the inhabitants reared them for the pot, having taken the eggs from the curassow's nests and hand-reared the chicks. The Spanish explorers thought that here

was an animal that could be domesticated to produce quantities of excellent flesh.

On the face of it, there seemed to be no reason why the curassows should not be bred in captivity. Its relatives, the chicken, pheasant, turkey and quail, had all been domesticated, and curassows might easily have won favour at festive occasions instead of the turkey. But the Spaniards found it impossible to breed them. First the curassow is a bird of the tropical forests and thickets, so warmth and seclusion are necessary. Also they live in trees rather than on the ground, and plenty of perching space is needed for them to remain healthy. Knowledge of these factors has allowed curassows to be bred in zoos in the United States and Europe, but, even so, one could never get rich quick by curassow farming when they lay only 2 or 3 eggs a year, compared with the turkey's 8–15 eggs.

class	**Aves**
order	**Galliformes**
family	**Cracidae**
genus & species	***Crax alector*** *crested curassow*
	C. rubra *great curassow*
	C. mitu *razor-billed curassow*
	C. pauxi *helmeted curassow*
	C. globulosa *red-wattled curassow*
	others

Great curassow (*Crax rubra*)

Razor-billed curassow (*C. mitu*)

Helmeted curassow (*C. pauxi*)

The curassow family is restricted to the warmer zones of the New World, and in South America they largely take the place of the pheasants which they resemble in many details. The great curassow, ranging from Mexico to Ecuador, weighs about 10½ lb. The helmeted curassows are alike in plumage—both are black and white, and both have a large helmet-shaped horny ridge on the base of the bill. The razor-billed curassow, which is called 'mutum' by the Brazilians, is black with a bluish sheen in both sexes, with brown on the belly and with a high frontal comb of the same red colour as the bill.

The well-camouflaged curlew is found on open moors, pastures or in woodland clearings and nests in a grass-filled hollow in low vegetation such as heather. The adult defends the nest and offspring vigorously, attacking even harriers and crows, or luring enemies away by feigning injury.

Curlew

The curlew gets its name from the two-syllable fluting call of the species common in Britain. Altogether there are eight birds belonging to the curlew genus, although some may be races of the same species. The common curlew is one of the larger waders, has streaky brown plumage and a characteristic 5in. down-curved bill. The whimbrel, or Hudsonian curlew, as it is called in North America, is very much like the curlew but is smaller and less shy. Other curlews are similar to the whimbrel in size and plumage, except the long billed curlew and the Madagascar curlew which are slightly larger than the common curlew.

The common curlew breeds from the British Isles, across Europe and Asia to China. The whimbrel is seen occasionally in Britain and a few pairs breed in the Orkneys and Shetlands. Its range, how-ever, is more northerly than that of the curlew with a discontinuous breeding range that includes Alaska, the west coast of Hudson's Bay, Iceland, Scandinavia, northern European Russia and Eastern Siberia. The long-billed curlew is the North American counterpart of the common curlew of Europe and Asia and used to breed over most of North America before farming diminished its range.

Curlews occur in Africa only as migrants,

the European curlew moving as far south as South Africa. The name Madagascar curlew is a misnomer. This bird breeds in eastern Siberia and migrates to Malaysia and Australia. It was named in error after the Macassar Straits near the Celebes, where the first specimen was collected.

Cosmopolitan migrators

Curlews are birds of open country, such as prairies, steppes, moors and marshes, where they may gather in large flocks numbering several hundred. They also migrate in flocks, and two species are noted for their long migrations. The Eskimo curlew, which is thought to belong to the same species as the little whimbrel of Australia and least curlew of Russia, breeds in the tundra of Alaska, then moves to Labrador and New-foundland to feed on the ripening crow-berries. When replete it flies south to the Argentinian pampas for the winter. Another traveller is the bristle-thighed curlew, named after the vaneless feathers on the thighs. It also breeds in Alaska and western Canada, but migrates 5 000 miles to the Hawaiian Islands in the Pacific.

Probing for food

Curlews feed on a variety of animals, to-gether with a few berries and seeds. Shell-fish, crustacea, insects, worms, fish and frogs are all eaten, depending on season and locality. In the British Isles cattle fields are searched for dung beetles from July to October, while in November they are deserted for stubble fields. Investigations in

Hungary showed that curlews and whim-brels were taking large numbers of harmful crickets and owlet moth caterpillars, and that 96% of the food of these whimbrels consisted of destructive insects. Shores, swamps and moors also provide sources of food, the curlews either picking it up from the surface of the ground or water, or prob-ing with their long bills for small animals living underground. Animals picked up in the tip of the bill are tossed to the mouth by jerks of the head.

The bristle-thighed curlew has the unusual habit, for a wader, of stealing eggs. While on the Pacific islands it steals eggs of terns, boobies and frigate birds, impaling them on its bill and carrying them away to be smashed and eaten at leisure.

Nesting in the open

The male defends his territory and ad-vertises for a mate by singing in the air. He flies low over the ground then rises vertically and hangs poised before drifting to the ground with wings outstretched, all the time pouring out his bubbling song.

The nests are grass-lined hollows in low vegetation such as heather and are found on open moors, pastures or in woodland clearings. Usually four eggs are laid, which are incubated by both parents for a month. The young are able to leave the nest shortly after hatching and they creep away to hide when not feeding with their parents.

The adult curlews defend their offspring vigorously, attacking harriers and crows, or luring enemies away by feigning injury. A long-billed curlew was once seen flopping

G Hakansson: Photo Res.

Speckled chicks hatch after a month's incubation.

Pamela Harrison

The curlew's flight is strong and rather gull-like with a measured beat.

W Puchalski: Photo Res.

It's a tight squeeze before hatching; having broken the shell the beak pokes out by the foot.

SC Porter: Photo Res.

Probers afield. On the shore curlews search for small crabs, shrimps and small fishes. Curlews eat some vegetable matter, picking food from the surface of the water or probing for it in sand.

along, as if with a broken wing, in front of a coyote. It kept just in front of the coyote, leaping ahead if the latter came too close, and was last seen leading it over a hill, at least half a mile from where it started.

Excitement with curlews

There was a time when vast flocks of Eskimo curlew in uncountable numbers used to migrate down the eastern side of North America, having gorged themselves on the crowberries of Labrador and New-foundland. They were called doughbirds because, when shot, their breasts split open on hitting the ground to reveal the soft, dough-like fat. A few years ago they were thought to be extinct, and it seemed that another bird had gone the way of the passenger pigeon. Both had existed in huge numbers but had been exterminated by a lust for killing. Hunters would go out shooting curlews, bringing down 20 or more with one shot, and when their waggons were loaded they would dump the contents and kill a second waggonful.

The story of the Eskimo curlew, however, has a happier ending than that of the passenger pigeon. In 1959 an Eskimo curlew was seen at Galveston Island, Texas, the first since 1945. Others have been seen since, so presumably there must still be a group breeding somewhere.

In 1948 another curlew caused excite-ment, but not because of its rarity. Bristle-thighed curlews were well known in their winter haunts, and it was known that they migrated up to Alaska, but no one knew

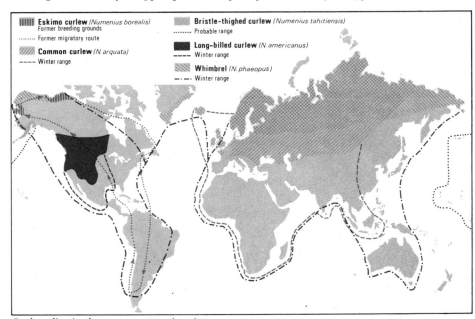

Eskimo curlew (*Numenius borealis*)	Bristle-thighed curlew (*Numenius tahitiensis*)
Former breeding grounds	Probable range
Former migratory route	Long-billed curlew (*N. americanus*)
Common curlew (*N. arquata*)	Winter range
Winter range	Whimbrel (*N. phaeopus*)
	Winter range

Curlews live in the open country migrating according to the seasons. The Eskimo and bristle-thighed curlews are noted for their long migrations.

where they bred. This curlew was the only bird in North America whose nest had never been seen, but in 1948 two members of a National Geographic Society expedition camped near the Yukon River, saw two bristle-thighed curlews continually return-ing to one place. They approached cauti-ously, then running forward they saw it fly off its well-concealed nest.

class	**Aves**
order	**Charadriiformes**
family	**Scolopacidae**
genus & species	***Numenius arquata*** *common curlew*
	N. phaeopus *whimbrel*
	N. borealis *Eskimo curlew*
	N. americanus *long-billed curlew*
	N. madagascariensis *Madagascar curlew*
	N. tahitiensis *bristle-thighed curlew*
	others

Australian spotted cuscus. Not a monkey but a pouched mammal related to the kangaroo. In both, the second and third toes of the hindfoot are bound together by skin and the claws are used for combing the fur.

Cuscus

The cuscus is an unusual phalanger that is often mistaken for a monkey. It has a rounded head, small ears almost buried in the fur, protruding yellow-rimmed eyes, short muzzle and yellow nose. About the size of a large domestic cat, 3½ ft long including a long prehensile tail, it makes good use of its voice. It has been suggested that its name refers to its scolding or 'cussing', but in fact it was originally **couscous,** *the French rendering of the aboriginal New Guinea name. There are over 16 species living in the forests of Queensland, Australia, and the jungles of New Guinea.*

Although monkey-like, especially in the face, a cuscus shows its relationship to kangaroos not only in the female having a pouch but also in the hindfoot. This is used for grasping branches and is more like a human hand, the long first toe being thumb-like and particularly strong. But the second and third toes are bound together by skin (that is, syndactylous) and their claws are used, as in kangaroos, for combing the fur.

Bouts of cussing

Cuscuses live in trees and are adept at clinging to branches with the hind feet and the prehensile tail, which can be wrapped round a branch for extra support when climbing. At rest, the tail is tightly coiled, like a watch spring.

When quarrelling among themselves or challenging another animal coming near it, the seemingly gentle and inoffensive cuscus will snarl and bark, in a guttural voice, in bursts of scolding. As it begins to bark it raises a forepaw in a menacing gesture, and if further provoked, strikes out with its front feet, perhaps even biting savagely, and all the time 'cussing'.

They live in thick cover, well hidden among foliage, keeping still by day. At night they move about among the trees feeding on leaves and insects, sometimes eating eggs and small birds. When feeding, a cuscus grips a branch with its back feet and tail, which leaves the front feet free for holding food. In captivity they will eat chopped fruit and vegetables.

Tightest sitter

The best-known species are the spotted cuscus, found in Queensland, and a second species of spotted cuscus in New Guinea in which the males and females are so unlike they were first thought to belong to different species. The female's fur is grey, brown or

Only rarely is a cuscus seen during the day, as it keeps still among thick foliage. At night it moves about branches feeding on leaves, insects and sometimes eggs and small birds. When feeding it grips the branch with its back feet and tail so the front feet are free for holding food.

fawn, a little lighter on the sides of the head. There is also a patch on the rump which is lighter still, and this is found in all cuscuses of whatever species and of both sexes. As the cuscus gets older this patch gets lighter because it is where the fur is worn down through the animal sitting so tight and so continuously through the day. There can be few animals to rival a cuscus for sitting tight.

By contrast with the female, the male spotted cuscus in New Guinea is a creamy white with many ½in. black spots uniformly spaced all over when young. As it grows older the black spots run into each other to form irregular grey blotches. The hind limbs also change to a uniform grey.

Little more is known about the life history or growth except that breeding must be fairly continuous. It is rare for a female to be found without at least one baby in the pouch.

There is little information on enemies either. One cuscus in captivity panicked at the approach of a python but this means little. Captive animals have often been seen to panic at the sight of strange objects which they could not possibly meet in their natural habitat.

One man's meat

Whether it is a defence or not, a cuscus has a strong and repulsive odour, and it is this very often that betrays its presence to the hunter. David Fleay, the distinguished Australian naturalist, has described how he returned from New Guinea with several cuscuses. The odour they gave out clung to every part of the ship the animals had occupied for a long time after they had been disembarked. Fleay himself handled them no more than he was compelled to and then very gingerly. Yet he tells how people edged

away from him in cinemas even after his suits had been twice cleaned.

In spite of the odour, Aborigines relish cuscus flesh, and they have a singularly callous way of ensuring a continuous supply of it fresh. When one of their hunters finds a cuscus he breaks its hindlegs so it can feed but cannot move far – a repulsive substitute for the kitchen 'fridge'.

class	**Mammalia**
order	**Marsupialia**
family	**Phalangeridae**
genus & species	***Phalanger nudicaudatus*** *Australian spotted cuscus* **P. maculatus** *New Guinea spotted cuscus others*

Cuttlefish

The cuttlefish is a mollusc related to octopuses and squids. Its body is shield-shaped, the margins forming two thin narrow fins. The relatively small head bears eight arms. It also has two long tentacles which, at rest, are retracted into a pocket beside each eye. The arms are then held together forming a cone with the apex directed forward. The arms are beset with suckers and there are suckers on the club-shaped ends of the tentacles. Each sucker is on a short muscular stalk and its rim is strengthened by a horny flange with serrated edge. The shell is internal. It is almost as long as the body and shield-shaped with a horny margin and its chalky centre is honey-combed with gas-filled chambers.

The common cuttlefish, the best known of the 80 species, was first described in detail by Aristotle, over 2 000 years ago. It ranges over the eastern North Atlantic, as far north as the North Sea, and into the Mediterranean. Its overall length is up to 3 ft, the body being up to 15 in. long. The smallest known cuttlefish is 1½ in. overall, the largest 5 ft. Most species of cuttle live in tropical or subtropical seas, mainly in shallow seas, but a few are deep-sea.

Jet propelled mollusc

Cuttlefish are capable of greater colour changes than any other mollusc, possibly greater and more rapid than any other animal. A cuttlefish swimming over a rock covered with weeds and sedentary animals of various colours will change from grey to reddish-brown and back again, to light brown or greenish, as it passes over the various patches of colour. Its ground colour is a creamy-grey, but embedded in the skin are bags of pigment known as chromatophores. These are highly elastic, and by the use of muscle fibres can be contracted or expanded. The pigments are mainly yellow, orange, brown, red and black and, by combination, a wide range of colours can be produced. Changes in colour can be produced in less than a second each, and a cuttlefish can pass from a deathly pallor to the black of a thundercloud almost in the twinkling of an eye. Cuttlefish swim in shoals. They swim and also change colour in unison, the stimulus for colour change being received through the eyes.

Cuttlefish move more slowly than octopuses but they keep on the move more. Their internal shell gives them buoyancy. They swim by undulations of the marginal fins, using the funnel on the underside of the body when speed is required. The funnel can eject a stream of water with force, driving the animal backwards with a form of jet propulsion. It can be turned in any direction, and the cuttlefish moves in the opposite direction to that in which the water is expelled. The funnel can also be used to maintain position. A cuttlefish apparently stationary just

△ *The cuttlefish has very large eyes similar in structure to those of a vertebrate. The skin contains pigment-filled chromatophores, which by changing their shape alter the colour of* **Sepia**.

▽ *Cuttlefish eggs looking like a bunch of grapes hatch into ½in. larvae still with their egg sacs.*

△ *The body of the cuttlefish is shield-shaped, the margins forming two narrow thin fins.*

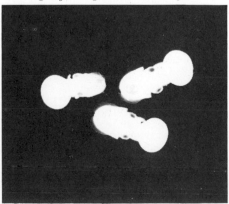

Klaus Paysan

Jane Burton: Photo Res.

Rotofilm

Rotofilm

576

Leisurely bottom swimmer

Right: The cuttlefish is a more leisurely swimmer than its relatives the squid and octopus. It hovers near to the bottom in inshore waters, feeding on shrimps and small fish which it stirs from the bottom by short jets of water from its funnel. The jets from the funnel are also used to move about. When speed is needed the cuttlefish ejects a stream of water through the funnel with force—a form of jet propulsion —and this drives the animal backwards. The funnel can be turned in any direction and is therefore used for steering and braking.

Below: By contracting the longitudinal muscles and relaxing the circular muscles, the mobile mantle enlarges so drawing in water which circulates round the gills.

Below right: When the circular muscles contract the mantle lobe is drawn in tight round the neck, and when the contraction has reached its height, water is forced out of the funnel. If the contractions are violent the ejection of the water causes quick jet propulsion.

Colin Doeg

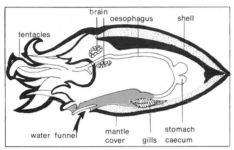

Cuttlefish in normal 'idling' position

Jet propulsion

Chris Howe I-Jones

beneath the surface can be seen constantly turning its funnel first in one direction, then in another, giving a brief puff each time. Together with the undulating fins, the effect of these gentle jets is to keep the cuttlefish more or less in one spot. The animal can also pivot on its own axis by making the fin on one side work in the reverse direction to the other, at the same time using the funnel to drive itself round.

The funnel is also used to eject blue-black 'ink'. Cuttlefish can quickly replenish their supply of this to give repeated ejections, enough to colour about 700 cu ft of water in a few minutes. Even tiny cuttlefish, just hatched, will eject ink when disturbed.

Hunting with tentacles

Cuttlefish feed by day on shrimps, prawns, crabs and fishes. The prey is stalked, and when close enough, the two tentacles are shot out with lightning speed and used like a pair of living tongs to bring food back to the mouth, which is armed with a horny parrot-like beak as well as a file-like tongue or radula. Care is taken to grip a crab from behind, and the crab is dropped if it can bring its claws to play. Large dead fish have been eaten. The cuttlefish tear them open with the beak before inserting the tong-like tentacles to remove pieces of flesh. These take 12 hours to be digested. Shrimps are flushed by the cuttlefish disturbing the sand with jets from its funnel. As the shrimps are exposed the tentacles grab them.

Enemies

The chief enemies are sharks, dolphins and porpoises. A cuttlefish can regenerate a lost arm, but not uncommonly whole shoals of them may litter the sea, or be cast ashore, badly mangled. It is not known what could cause this.

Colourful courtship

Mating takes place in spring and summer. Then the cuttlefish put on a courting dress, a kind of zebra pattern, more brightly defined in males than females. At this time one of the arms on the left side of the male becomes modified. It loses some of the suckers near the base and is then used to transfer sperm to the female. The females are said to be luminous during the mating period. The eggs are laid singly. They pass out through the funnel, being there fertilised, and coated with a latex-like solution which is coloured with a squirt of ink. Each capsule formed by the hardening of the solution bears a long stalk. The stalks of the eggs are entwined on a support by the female, or she may tangle stalks of a succession of eggs on each other to form bunches of capsules. These often come adrift and are seen cast up on the beach, looking like bunches of grapes. Each female lays up to 300 eggs in batches of 20–30. The young cuttlefish when hatched is about ½ in. long, resembling the parent except for its larger head and eyes. It feeds on copepods.

All's fair in love and fishing

Three thousand years ago cuttlefish were caught in the Mediterranean by jigging and by torchlight and trident. They still are today. Three thousand years ago female cuttlefishes were lured to lay their eggs on branches placed in the water just offshore. Much the same method is used today. The males follow the spawning females, and once the eggs are laid the fishermen swoop. This seems unfair, but there is more to come. Of the several other methods used to catch cuttlefish for the table, one involves putting a hook through the skin of a female cuttlefish and towing her so that she rides about 6 ft below the surface. One after another the males swim in to her. Hardly have they embraced when both are lifted from the water with a net. He is disentangled and kept. She is put back to entice yet another suitor to his doom.

phylum	**Mollusca**
class	**Cephalopoda**
order	**Decapoda**
family	**Sepiidae**
genus & species	*Sepia officinalis*

577

The dab is a fish that lies on its side, has a twisted mouth, and an eye that migrates round the head to lie on the same side as the other eye.

Dab

The dab is a small flatfish that lives in the shallow seas of western Europe including the Baltic. It reaches a maximum length of 17½ in. and may be recognized by the brown colour of the upper surface and by the shape of the lateral line, which is strongly curved opposite the pectoral fin. There are red spots like those on a plaice but smaller. The flattened body is fringed by the long dorsal and anal fins, the pectorals and pelvics being reduced to almost nothing. The scales on the upper surface are toothed on the rear margin and rough to the touch. The undersurface of the dab is white and its scales have smooth margins. Individuals sometimes turn up on which both upper and lower surfaces are coloured and in these the scales on the undersurface also feel rough.

The dab is inferior to the plaice as a sea-food and does not keep so well. Nevertheless it is eaten, especially where it can be cooked soon after capture.

The long rough dab of the west European and North American coasts, to about latitude 40 degrees south, is more nearly related to the flounder.

A fish that lies on its side

The dab is a fish that lies on its side, has a twisted mouth, and an eye that migrates round the head. It is found in enormous numbers in sandy bays, including those about an inch long that have just completed their free-swimming life and settled on the bottom. It lives close inshore, particularly in September, when it is caught in large numbers in shrimp trawls or push nets. Its habits are similar to those of the plaice, with which it tends to compete for food, except that it keeps inshore for most of the year, whereas plaice tend to move offshore for part of the year.

Bottom feeding fish

The dab also has especially strong teeth in the lower jaw which enable it to take a wider range of food. It eats almost any small bottom-living invertebrates: starfish, crabs, molluscs and worms.

The dab is not an active fish. It spends long periods merely lying on the seabed. When moving over the bottom it may use the long dorsal and anal fins fringing the body to get a grip to move forward slowly, or it may, by undulating these, progress at a fair speed. Indeed, a dab when disturbed can shoot through the water, a little off the bottom, with surprising speed.

Born normal, becomes a freak

The spawning season is from March to May, when each female lays 80—130 thousand eggs, each 32/1000 in. diameter. These float at the surface and hatch in 3—12 days according to the temperature of the water; the warmer it is the more quickly the embryo develops. Each egg is well supplied with yolk, and the newly-hatched fish, then 1/100 in. long, carries on its underside the remains of the yolksac. Mouth, jaws and digestive tract are not developed for a further 10—11 days, during which time the baby dabs are using up the yolk.

At first the young dab, having absorbed the yolksac and begun to feed on very small plankton, looks like the young of any other fish. That is, its body is rounded, it has fins in the usual places, and it has an eye on either side of its head. But its jaws soon become twisted and during the next 2—4 months further remarkable transformations take place. The dorsal and anal fins in normal fishes are relatively small and serve mainly as balancers. In the dab, and related flatfishes, they become very long, running down either side of the body, and they are the main organs for swimming. At the same time as the dorsal and anal fins are enlarging, the body of the fish becomes flattened from side-to-side and the dab lies on one side. What was formerly the right side becomes the upper surface and the left side becomes the lower surface.

The most astonishing change is in the left eye, which migrates round the head to lie alongside the right eye, so that in the mature dab instead of an eye either side of the body there are two eyes near each other looking upwards. In addition a thick dark lobe forms over each eye covering the upper part of the pupil, shielding it from the light coming from above.

Flattened fishes

The term flatfish is also applied to the skates and rays, related to sharks, in which there is a much simpler type of flattening, from above downwards. In the dab and in its relatives such as the plaice, sole and flounder, which are bony or true fishes, the bodies are flattened from side-to-side. The end result is much the same, that a fish is evolved which is adapted to living and feeding on the seabed. In the skates and rays, this end is achieved with relatively little disturbance. In the flatfishes proper, as represented by the dab, there have been drastic changes: a flattening and a twisting so that many parts of the body, the eyes and the jaws especially, have had to undergo radical changes.

One of the most interesting steps in this series of changes in the dab has to do with the migration of the left eye. Although the skull as well as the rest of the skeleton is made of bone, it starts off as softer cartilage. In the newly-hatched dab there is a bar of cartilage above each eye. Very soon after this the cartilage above the left eye is absorbed, so the eye can travel over the top of the head and on to the right side.

class	**Pisces**
order	**Pleuronectiformes**
family	**Pleuronectidae**
genus & species	*Limanda limanda*

Daddy long-legs

Daddy long-legs, or crane flies, are familiar thin-bodied insects with long thread-like legs, which are about in great numbers throughout much of the summer, flying at varying heights and often at the mercy of high winds. The male is readily recognized because the end of his abdomen is widened and clubbed, while the female's is drawn out to form a pointed ovipositor (egg-laying organ). In the United States the name daddy long-legs is applied to a different creature, the harvestman or harvester, a relative of spiders. This will be dealt with later. Both have long legs which are easily lost but there the similarity ends. There are nearly 300 species of daddy long-legs in Britain alone.

The larvae of daddy long-legs are the troublesome leatherjackets of garden and pasture. These long, soft, fat grubs without legs feed on roots, including grasses, which is why they can ruin a lawn so easily and become greatly disliked.

Root pests

Adult crane flies do not feed much. Their mouthparts are modified into a snout-like proboscis with which they suck water and nectar. Most of the feeding is done by the larva or leatherjacket which, fully grown, is over 1½ in. long, greyish and repulsive. Immediately the larvae hatch they begin to feed, using their very strong jaws to eat the roots and lower stems of plants, notably grass, but also cultivated plants such as mangolds, oats and potatoes. The effect of a heavy infestation of leatherjackets on grassland may be to produce extensive bare brown patches. Gardeners and groundsmen sometimes combat leatherjackets by placing large groundsheets over lawns. The larvae often come above ground at night to feed on grass stems, so covering the ground by day induces them to rise to the surface as if it were night. After a while the covering is removed and the larvae swept up in their hundreds.

Aquatic crane fly larvae feed on small worms, dragonfly larvae and any other insect larvae which are available.

Larvae must have water

The commonest British species is the large greyish bodied *Tipula oleracea* which is particularly common in late summer. They often fly low over the ground with their long legs trailing passively, and because of this many are caught in the webs of garden spiders. The males of some of the smaller species swarm in nuptial flights before mating. Eggs are laid in water, damp earth, moss or saturated wood, and the larvae and pupae are aquatic or semi-aquatic. Those species most troublesome to man which live on land also require moisture, so that periods of drought often kill off the larvae in large numbers.

Breeding may continue through much of the year. Females which lay their eggs in spring or early summer, having themselves emerged from overwintering pupae, may

Stephen Dalton: NHPA

△ *The daddy long-legs is a familiar insect during summer months in garden and countryside.*

▽ *Before mating, males of smaller species swarm in nuptial flights. Eggs are laid in water.*

Gordon F Woods: NHPA

The daddy long-legs has only one pair of wings, the rear pair being reduced to club-shaped rods called halteres. These can be clearly seen above.

◁ This female daddy long-legs **Nephrotoma crocata** shows the pointed ovipositor at the abdomen's tip. The end of the male's abdomen is club-shaped.

JAL Cooke

give rise to a further generation in a matter of weeks. On emerging from the pupa, the male *Tipula oleracea* immediately seeks a mate. Often the males emerge some time before the females and this may mean a long, drawn out search for a partner. Occasionally a male will wait as a female emerges from her pupal case and mate with her while her skin is still soft and damp.

The female lays her tiny, black, seed-like eggs by thrusting her ovipositor deep into the soil. From about June onwards she may lay up to 100 eggs which hatch in about a fortnight. The small larvae, with wrinkled and flexible skins, are exceedingly tough. The larva feeds and increases in size by shedding its skin to form the familiar leatherjacket. Finally it changes to the pupa, and as the time for emergence approaches the pupa wriggles towards the surface of the ground helped by downwardly pointing bristles on its body, and thrusts itself part way out. Then the pupal skin splits behind the head and along the lines of the wings, and the adult fly forces its way out. Dozens of delicate brownish pupal cases can sometimes be seen on a lawn.

The aquatic larvae have five pairs of false legs, lost when the insect becomes an adult, which enable them to crawl about the bottoms of ponds and streams. They breathe by taking oxygen dissolved in the water, or by rising to the surface at intervals to take in air. The pupae remain active, and have two horn-like processes on the head, with which to take in air from above the surface of the water.

Gyroscopic flight control

Like all flies, the daddy long-legs has only one pair of wings, the second, rear pair being reduced to two club-shaped rods called halteres. In small flies such as a blowfly or housefly, halteres are difficult to see, but in the large daddy long-legs they are easily visible. Halteres was the name given to the two weights or bags of sand that Ancient Greek athletes held in each hand to help throw themselves forward in the long jump. The name is appropriate to the vestigal wings of flies for they are used to balance the flies in flight.

While a fly is in the air, its halteres are rapidly vibrated in the same figure of eight motion as the wings, and in doing so they act in the same way as the gyroscopes which are the basis of an automatic pilot. Rotating at great speed, a gyroscope in a plane stays level while fuselage rolls, yaws and pitches about it. Instruments attached to the gyroscope measure the degree of movement and automatically inform the controls of the steps needed to bring the plane back on to course.

Halteres function in much the same way. At the base of each are sense organs that detect strains and stresses put on the base of the halteres as the fly changes course. If you were so callous as to cut the halteres off a fly, it would have great difficulty in flying. A housefly would be unable to remain airborne but a daddy long-legs would still be able to fly after a fashion, because its long legs and long thin abdomen help to steady it. The housefly could later be restored to normal flight by gluing a thread of cotton to its abdomen to act as a tailplane.

phylum	**Arthropoda**
class	**Insecta**
order	**Diptera**
family	**Tipulidae**
genus	*Tipula*, others

581

Damselfish

Most damselfishes, or demoiselles, live in shallow tropical waters, especially around coral reefs. Many are brightly coloured, as shown by their names, such as the orange-coloured garibaldi and the blue chromis, and some, such as the sergeant major, are spotted or striped. The majority are less than 6 in. long. The body is deep, somewhat flattened from side-to-side with prominent dorsal fins, the front one of which is spinous.

Quarrelsome demoiselles

Many damselfishes live near coral reefs, hovering close to the coral heads, perhaps several hundred at a time. When disturbed they dart with one accord into the crevices among the corals. Damselfishes living in temperate seas, the garibaldi of the Bay of California, for example, live over the kelp beds or on rocky coasts, places offering shelter equivalent to that of coral reefs. Many others tend to take up station near large anemones and this has led in several cases to either a loose or a close symbiosis between the fish and the anemone. This reaches an extreme in the often quoted association between the giant anemone and the small clownfish.

A peculiarity of the family is that some species use their pectoral fins almost like oars. They are brought forward almost edgewise and pulled back more or less broadside on.

Damselfishes are often aggressive, with a strong territorial sense. Some live in pairs once they mature and are aggressive towards others of their kind using their particular shelters or going anywhere near them. Their aggressiveness is expressed largely by clicking noises made with teeth lining the throat, the pharyngeal teeth. In fact, these small attractive fishes seem more deserving to be called amazons than damsels. As is usual in fishes, the strong territorial instinct is linked with a marked degree of parental care.

Carnivorous damsels

The feeding habits of damselfishes are not well known. They seem to be carnivorous, feeding mainly on smaller fishes, even the weaker ones of their own kind, especially if there are not enough places in which the small ones may hide.

Prolific breeders

Breeding in the spotted damselfish of the Indo-Pacific has been studied by Dr J Garnaud. He kept these in the Aquarium at Monaco and found that each pair spawned in the early morning, as often as three times a month, and at each spawning the female laid 20–25 thousand eggs. These are sticky and are laid in small clusters, on rocks or other firm surfaces. The male guards the eggs until they hatch 4–5 days later.

The garibaldi, another damselfish studied, spawns at depths of 4–12 ft. Before spawning, the male cleans an area of rock around a clump of red seaweed, and on this the female lays her eggs. The young garibaldi

△ *Clown fish sport among the tentacles of anemones growing on a coral reef.*
▽ *Garibaldi, the charmingly-named **Hypsypops rubicunda**. This youngster will later lose his blue spots and become a brilliant orange.*

▷ *Dangerous landlord: this anemone has become used to the attentions of these two clown fish. It takes time for a clown fish to be 'accepted' by an anemone—and until this happens the fish is literally dicing with death.*

Blue demoiselles **Chromis caerulea** *swarm past a coral reef in the Seychelles, Indian Ocean. Damselfish or demoiselles are found in shallow tropical waters around the world, especially near coral reefs.*

is orange-red with blue blotches which begin to disappear when the fishes reach a length of about 2½ in. and are completely gone by the time they are adult.

Living with death

The best known damselfish is the clown anemone fish which shelters among the tentacles of a giant anemone which can reach up to 4 ft across. There are other damselfishes that have this habit but the clown fish is the one most often quoted. It may leave the anemone to swim around but at first alarm dashes back to take refuge among the tentacles. It is claimed that when the fish darts back to the shelter of the anemone's tentacles any fish pursuing it will be caught and held by the tentacles, the clown fish receiving fragments from the anemone's meal.

Years ago it was supposed that the stinging cells were brought into action the moment anything touched them. Then it

was realized that they were more selective. They are not discharged if, for example, any kind of plant material touches them. Now we know that the slime on the scales of a clown fish inhibits the stinging cells. But this is not the end of the story.

When a giant anemone and its clown fish are placed in an aquarium the fish seems to recognise the anemone and quickly swims towards it. Then it circles the anemone, getting nearer and nearer to it until it is close enough to nibble its body. It does this several times then it swims over the tentacles and eventually touches one or two of them. Having done this it immediately races away. Later it returns and again touches the tentacles. This is repeated several times, and each time the tentacles of the anemone can be seen sticking to the fish, showing that the stinging cells have been discharged at it. Finally the fish swims deeper into the tentacles, which no longer cling to it. The fish and the anemone were becoming used to each other's company. It seems as if the

anemone must get to know its own particular damselfish, perhaps becoming immunised, as it were.

By contrast, if a clown fish living with one anemone is removed and placed with another anemone it is stung and killed. But a pair of clown fishes may raise a family among the tentacles, the father guarding the offspring until they are old enough to go out and find their own anemones. What we do not know is how the acquaintance between a damselfish and an anemone is struck in the first place.

class	**Pisces**
order	**Perciformes**
family	**Pomacentridae**
genera & species	***Abudefduf saxatilis*** *sergeant major* ***Amphiprion percula*** *clown fish* ***Chromis cyanea*** *blue chromis* ***Hypsypops rubicunda*** *garibaldi* *others*

Familiar to tiddler-fishing children as 'blue arrows', damselflies are never found far from the water where they breed. Their wings are long and weakly-muscled, and—as this male demonstrates—they are held over the back when the insect rests, like those of butterflies.

Damselfly

A damsel was originally a woman of noble birth or stately position, elegant and well-dressed, and this is why smaller relatives of dragonflies are called damselflies. Smaller on average than dragonflies and far more slender, they hold their wings when at rest elegantly erect over the back, like a butterfly. Their flight is weak and fluttering and many are brightly coloured, blue, red or metallic green. The wings may be colourless and transparent or variously and often beautifully tinted. In some species the males have coloured and patterned wings while those of the female are transparent. The early stages of almost all damselflies are passed in water.

Although the term 'dragonfly' is often used as equivalent to the insect order Odonata, the two main suborders, Zygoptera *and* Anisoptera, *are better designated by separate English names, damselfly and dragonfly respectively.*

Fastidious insect

Damselflies have only a weak flight and so are seldom found far from the water in which they breed. Ponds, ditches and canals with a thick growth of reeds and water plants are their favourite haunts, and bulldozers and mechanical dredgers are now their most serious enemies.

Most insects often clean the eyes and antennae with the forelegs, much as a cat 'washes its face'. Damselflies are particularly given to this. They not only clean the sense organs of the head but use the hindlegs to clean the end of the abdomen. Frequently the abdomen itself is curved and raised so as to stroke the wings and divide them from each other. The most likely reason for this is that the long and weakly muscled wings are liable to get stuck together by drifting threads of spider gossamer.

A damsel courted

Some kinds of damselflies perform courtship displays before mating. In the banded agrion *Agrion splendens* the male waits for a female to fly past and signals to her by raising his body and spreading his wings. If this succeeds and she comes to rest near him he performs an aerial fluttering dance backwards and forwards, facing her all the time, and then comes to rest and mates with her. The banded agrion is one of the species in which the wings are conspicuously coloured in the male and not in the female, and it seems likely that this difference in the sexes is associated with courtship display.

The method of mating used by damselflies (and dragonflies) is unique among insects. The opening of the male's internal sexual organs is in the usual insect position, near the tip of the abdomen. Before mating he transfers sperm to a complicated accessory sexual organ on the underside of the front part of the abdomen, just behind the thorax. When pairing he first grasps the female's

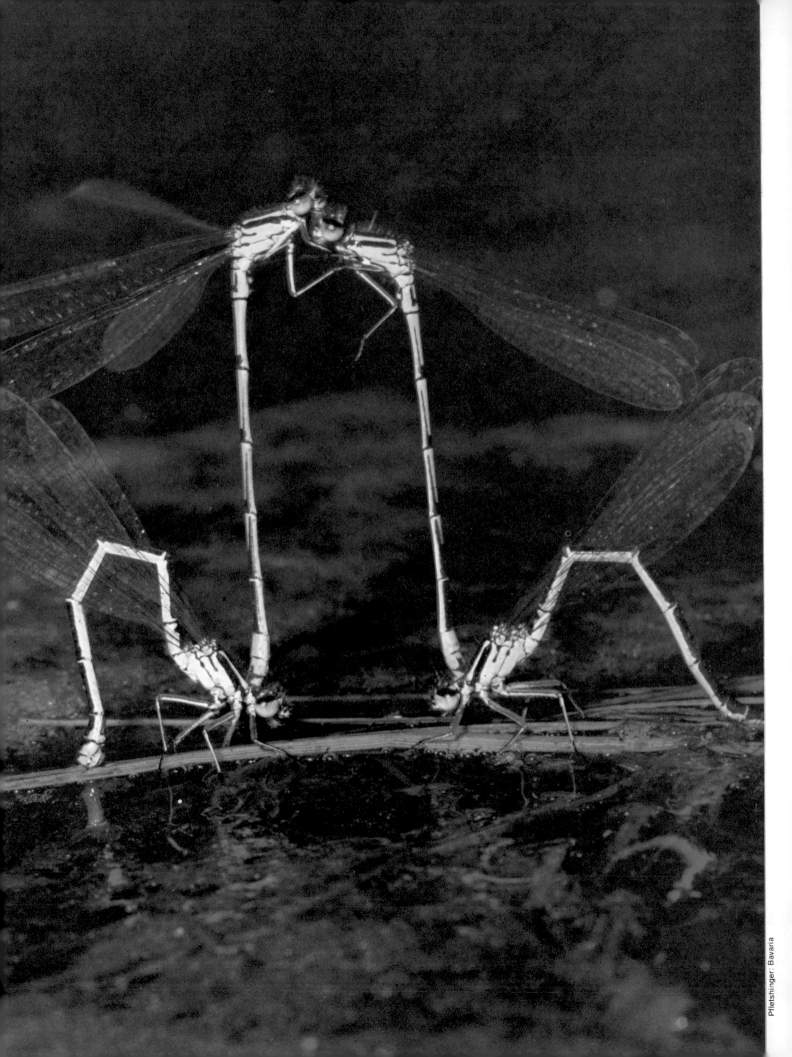

△ *Flying damselfly demonstrates its out-of-phase wingbeat motion. Damselflies are noted for their weak, fluttering flight.*
◁ *Confused encounter: two damselfly couples, indulging in pre-mating display, form a bewildering pattern for the camera.*

head or prothorax with a pair of claspers at the tip of his abdomen. Both then bend their bodies so as to bring the end of the female's abdomen into contact with the male accessory organ, and the sperm is transferred.

The fertilised eggs are laid through a saw-like ovipositor, in the tissues of water plants. This often takes place immediately after mating, and sometimes before the male has released his hold on the female. In some species the two, coupled in this way, crawl down the stem of a reed into the water and descend together to a depth of a foot or more before the eggs are laid.

Life cycle

The minute creature that hatches from a damselfly egg can neither swim nor crawl and is known as the prolarva or pronymph. Within a few minutes, sometimes almost immediately after hatching, it sheds its skin and the first active larval stage is produced. This larva spends its life in the water and grows in the usual insect fashion, by shedding its skin at intervals. It has a long body, not unlike that of an adult damselfly in shape, but of course no wings. At its hinder end are three leaf-like external gills. These contain a network of minute tubes, or tracheae, into which oxygen diffuses from

the water. Respiration also takes place through the skin, rectum and wing sheaths.

The life cycle of most of the smaller British damselflies takes a year to complete, that of some of the larger ones two years. In the tropics, development is more rapid and there may be several generations in a year. When growth is complete the larva crawls out of the water up a stone or rush stem, waits for a short time until the skin of the back splits, and the mature damselfly emerges. The wings are expanded and hardened and the insect can fly within an hour or two.

Although damselfly larvae are usually aquatic, in Hawaii there are a few species, of the genus *Megalagrion*, whose larvae spend all or part of their time on land. In one of these *M. oahuense* the leaf-like tail gills are replaced by hairy appendages and the larva is unable to swim.

Rapacious beauties

Adults feed on small insects, both in the air and at rest, and the larvae probably eat small water insects, worms and the like. Adults, although neither swift nor strong, can 'hawk' small flying insects, as dragonflies often do. They probably feed mainly on gnats and midges.

Spirit of the dead

People who go out collecting insects have never been rated highly by the general public. At the same time, nobody has treated them with worse than amused tolerance, except in parts of tropical America. Most damselflies are much smaller than dragonflies, but the largest damselflies are greater than the largest dragonflies. One of these huge damselflies *Megaloprepus coerulatus* is 5 in. long and has a wingspan of 7 in. When these damselflies fly in the dusk of the tropical forest they are hardly visible, except for the coloured wing tips. This ghost-like appearance has led the aboriginal people to believe that they are the departed spirits of the dead, and they strongly object to their being hunted by collectors.

phylum	**Arthropoda**
class	**Insecta**
order	**Odonata**
suborder	**Zygoptera**
genera	*Agrion, Megalagrion* *others*

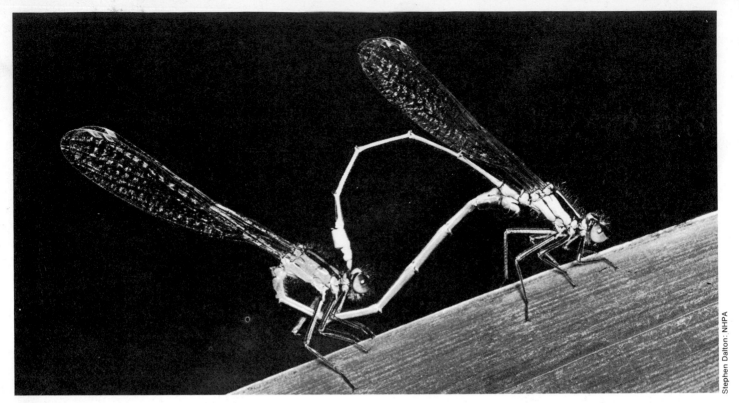

△ *Mating procedure: the male (right) grips the female's thorax with the claspers at the tip of his abdomen; the female bends her abdomen forward to bring it into contact with the secondary sexual organ beneath the male's thorax.*

◁ *Interim phase: a damselfly nymph, showing the three leaf-like gills at its hind end.*

▽ *Three-stage birth of the damselfly. Left: The nymph crawls out of the water onto a convenient sedge. Centre: The skin on the nymph's back splits and the damselfly starts to crawl out. Right: Once clear of the husk of its former self, the damselfly waits for its wings to harden.*

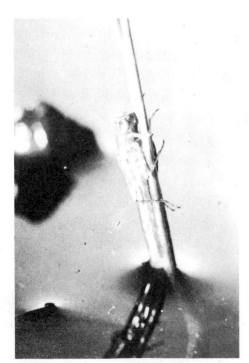

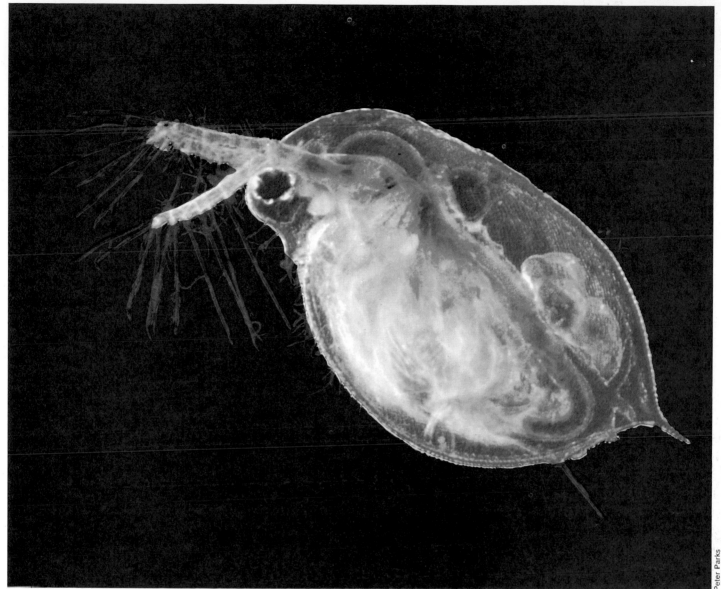

Daphnia, with its long branched antennae, is covered by a large transparent folded carapace, protecting its five pairs of food-gathering limbs, each limb being designed for a certain task. The heart is seen just above the brood pouch, between the fold of the carapace and the dark curved gut.

Daphnia

Daphnia, the water flea, the largest species of which is only ⅕ in. long, has been the subject of many fascinating studies. It is familiar, in dried form, to anyone who has kept goldfish. They are often seen as a cloud of dancing specks in pond or aquarium, or even as a surface scum. Daphnia are crustaceans, distant relatives of crabs and shrimps. They have a hard external skeleton and jointed bodies and limbs. The head has a large central eye which is really two eyes joined together. It also has two pairs of antennae, one small and the other large, which are branched and used in swimming.

There are five pairs of limbs, in constant motion, each flattened and bearing a complex arrangement of feathered bristles. These limbs lie in a space under the body bounded by the carapace which looks like the shell of a bivalve mollusc. This also forms a brood pouch in the female. The

transparency of the carapace makes it possible to watch the internal organs at work, the little heart pumping the blood, which may be red with oxygen-carrying haemoglobin. At its hind end the carapace is drawn out into a spine.

There are about 25 British species in the family Daphniidae. The largest, **Daphnia magna,** *local in distribution, also occurs in North America. Some species may be abundant enough in water works to choke the filters.*

A life of ups and downs

Daphnia spends much of its time bobbing up and down in the water head uppermost, sinking down a short way then driving itself up again with a downward stroke of its large branched antennae. Like many other creatures living in the upper waters of seas and lakes, Daphnia also migrates up and down every day to different depths. At dusk, the movement is upward, but during the night the whole population may gradually sink, only to rise again at dawn. Then, as the sun shines more brightly, it once more

retreats to deeper water. Jacques Loeb, a pioneer student of the behaviour of lower animals, found a change in the reaction of Daphnia to light after he had poured beer into the aquarium. A more instructive experiment, also performed by Loeb, easier to interpret and less wasteful, is to add a little carbonated water. The Daphnia then react by swimming towards the light, and in nature this response would have the value of taking them away from regions of excessive carbon dioxide and insufficient oxygen.

Similarly, Daphnia in a jar of water will tend to swim downward if the jar is shaken, a response that would normally take them towards safety. If this is done a number of times, the response may gradually wane as if the animals were getting used to it. If, however, the jar is now more vigorously shaken it will send them again towards the bottom.

When Daphnia sees red

Daphnia feeds on bacteria and single-celled algae floating in the water. It must filter large amounts of water to strain these particles, and it does this by rhythmic beat-

589

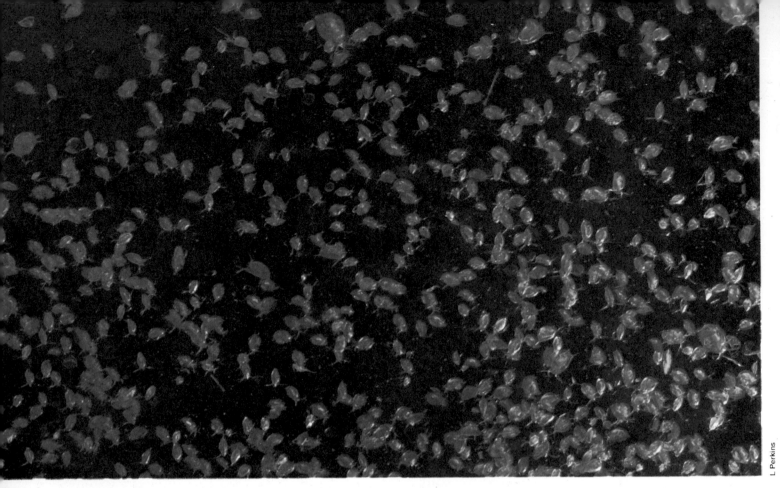

L Perkins

Like copepods, the cladocera water-fleas to which Daphnia belongs are classed with the lower crustacea. Water-flea swarms make up the chief part of freshwater plankton, which is a staple food of some fishes and other small aquatic animals. Daphnia feeds on bacteria and algae living in the water.

ing of its legs, pumping water through the space under its carapace, using the bristles on the legs as strainers.

It is clearly an advantage for Daphnia to stay where the algae are densest. This is done by sight, but not by spotting food at a distance and heading straight for it. When Daphnia is exposed to red light in the laboratory, it will spend much of its time 'dancing' upright in the water and moving horizontally very little. In blue light it tends to swim horizontally. When sunlight shines through a patch of green algae in the water much of the blue light is removed so the light passing through is redder. If Daphnia arrives by chance among algae, the slight redness of the light will cause it to 'dance' in that spot, therefore not move away. Otherwise, the tendency is to swim horizontally, so improving the chance of finding food.

Not much use for males

The life cycle of Daphnia is notable for the female carrying her eggs in a brood-pouch and for the way she lays eggs at certain times that can survive drying and freezing to hatch out months or years later. These are known as resting eggs. Another peculiarity is that males appear at only certain times when conditions are favourable.

The resting eggs carry the populations over the winter. They hatch in spring to give a generation of females only. These grow after each moult. Moults occur daily at first and average 17 during life.

After each moult the animal swells by taking in water before growing a new skin (cuticle). After 5–7 moults, a female begins

to lay up to 30 eggs, which develop without being fertilised. They are kept in the brood-pouch, the growing embryos being nourished by the yolk in the egg and also by secretions from the mother's body. As the season advances, the water warms up, the number of algae increases, growth of the Daphnia speeds up, and the population of females increases.

With the rise in population, food becomes short and males are hatched, less than half the size of the females and slightly different in shape. Now any eggs laid are fertilised and these are of the resting type. They are fewer per female, larger and thick-shelled. Part of the carapace containing them forms a protective case and this, with the eggs inside, is shed at the next moult.

As summer ends the number of algae again increases, the population builds up, there is overcrowding and more males appear. Resting eggs are once more produced, and these survive the winter to restart the population next spring. A few females may last the winter too. Living less actively at a low temperature, these grow largest and live longest. Only unsuitable conditions cause the appearance of males and resting eggs, not time of year, and hundreds of generations can be reared without any males appearing.

Bad conditions make Daphnia blush

In some species of Daphnia there may be great changes in the appearance of individual animals. So great may these changes

be that, until they were recognized in about 1890, individuals of a single species, indeed of a single population, were assigned to different genera. Some of the changes are due to age and reproductive condition, and to changes in the environment, but most dramatic are the annual changes in form, a condition known as 'cyclomorphosis'. The kind of thing that can happen is that the winter form will have a small head with the eye at the front, while in the summer form that part of the head in front of the eye grows forwards as a long 'helmet'.

Another factor that may cause individuals to vary in appearance is the amount of oxygen in the water. When man lives for a while at high altitude, so that the air he breathes contains less oxygen, his body is stimulated to produce more haemoglobin to carry oxygen in the blood from lungs to tissues. Changes in Daphnia living in poorly aerated water are visible in the colour of the body, there being as much as a twelve-fold increase in the haemoglobin as opposed to an increase of only about a fifth in man at high altitude. The warmer the water, or the less oxygen there is in it, the redder become the Daphnia.

phylum	**Arthropoda**
class	**Crustacea**
order	**Cladocera**
family	**Daphniidae**
genus & species	***Daphnia magna*** *others*

Darter

Darters are also known as snakebirds, from their sinuous form. Very much like cormorants in shape, they have longer, more slender necks, usually carried in a Z-shaped posture, and long stiletto-like bills. In America they are known as anhingas, a word coming from the language of Amazonian Indians. They are very closely related to the cormorants (p 527), and some scientists consider they both belong to the same family.

The plumage is generally dark with a metallic sheen, and the female usually has paler underparts. There are four species of darter that differ considerably in colour, but are otherwise very similar. The American anhinga ranges from the southern borders of the United States to Argentina. The African darter is found in Africa south of the Sahara, the Middle East and Madagascar; the Indian darter lives in India and southeast Asia and the Australian darter in Australia and New Guinea. They are strong fliers and in some areas are migratory.

Freshwater divers

Unlike their relatives the cormorants, that live mainly in coastal waters, darters inhabit freshwater lakes, rivers and swamps. They stay around the wooded edges and banks, where they may be seen perching in the trees with their wings spread like cormorants. Only rarely are they seen in the brackish waters of estuaries and lagoons. Darters are strong swimmers, propelling themselves with their webbed feet, their heads jerking to and fro in the manner of a pigeon, but much magnified by the length of the neck.

On the surface, darters often swim with only head and neck showing, for, like divers and grebes, they can change their buoyancy. This is achieved by two methods. The plumage can be flattened against the body, so squeezing out air trapped between the feathers. This air is essential to all water birds to keep them fully afloat. If a duck, for instance, has the waterproofing layer of oil removed from its feathers by detergent, it loses most of its buoyancy and floats with only head and neck showing. Diving birds can also reduce their buoyancy by exhaling air from the air sacs. These are a series of thin-walled, balloon-like extensions of the lungs that spread through the body. They are known to play an important part in the bird's breathing system but how they function is not known.

Spear fishers

Darters hunt underwater for fish, frogs, newts, crustaceans and water insects. Large prey is caught by impaling it on the bill with a quick strike of the head. After catching the prey, the darter surfaces and throws it off the bill, with a quick flick of the head, and catches it deftly, then juggles to line it up for swallowing. The whole action is remarkably skilful and, although basically instinctive, its perfection needs practice. Young

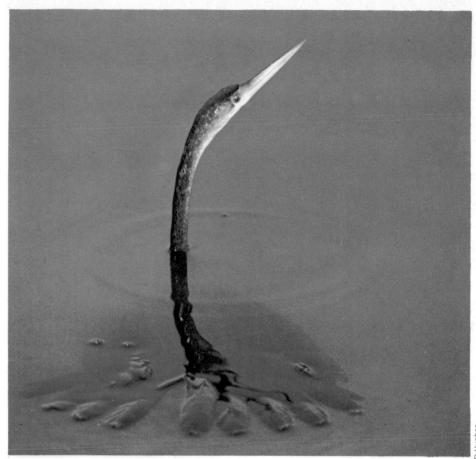

D Hughes

△ *The snake-necked darter will often swim at 'periscope-depth', with its body submerged. This is done by exhaling air from the body's air sacs, or by flattening the plumage and squeezing out trapped air.*

▽ *Darters resemble cormorants in hunting fish underwater, and also in posing with wings extended. They frequent wooded edges and banks of lakes and streams.*

D Hughes

591

Last stage but one. After hunting this fish underwater and impaling it on its bill with a spear-gun jab of its neck muscles, this darter is juggling its next meal into alignment before swallowing. If too firmly impaled, the prey becomes an embarrassment and is often lost.

D Hughes

darters can be seen having difficulty in removing fish that are firmly speared, or losing them when they are shaken off.

This spear-fishing technique does not allow darters to catch the largest and most agile fish, and even those caught often need to be subdued by being beaten against a branch before they can be swallowed.

The darters' stomachs have an unusual matted hair-like lining. The function of this is not known but it is suggested that it may be used to strain out fish bones which are then regurgitated.

Nesting in trees
Darters nest in small colonies in trees and bushes, usually overhanging water and sometimes only a few feet above it. They frequently nest in the same trees as herons and ibises.

The same nests are often used year after year but it is not unusual for a colony to shift from one part of a lake or river to another in succeeding years. When old nests are being used, the males claim them at the beginning of the breeding season and defend them against rivals. After the birds have paired off, they repair the nests by adding more sticks and a lining of leaves.

To attract a female to his nest, a male darter slowly waves his wings, stretching and closing each one alternately to show off their conspicuous colouring. Having attracted a female and courted her he collects twigs from nearby trees and bushes which she weaves into the nest.

Both parents incubate 3—6 eggs for about a month. The chicks hatch out naked and blind but within a short time grow coats of white down. In 2 weeks they will leave the nest, if disturbed, to plunge into the water and swim away. When the danger is over they will try to climb back to the nest, or failing that, scramble out onto a rock or log, using their neck and wings as well as their feet. The parents will continue to feed them in their new refuge until they are fledged, at 6—8 weeks.

The first spear-gun

As a darter stalks up to its prey it moves its neck to and fro like an athlete poising to throw the javelin, then thrusts its head forward in a lightning strike by straightening its neck. The speed of the strike is obtained by a trigger mechanism in the characteristic Z-shape of the neck, which is built like an

extendable arm with two joints, either side of the eighth vertebrae. These joints cannot be straightened out completely without tearing muscles or tendons, but they can bend a considerable amount. To strike, the darter draws its head back by tendons running the length of the neck, and passing through a 'pulley' mechanism on one of the vertebrae just behind the joints. Then, having aimed, the head is shot forward by a powerful muscle straightening the joints.

class	**Aves**
order	**Pelecaniformes**
family	**Anhingidae**
genus & species	***Anhinga anhinga*** *American anhinga*
	A. rufa *African darter*
	A. melanogaster *Indian darter*
	A. novaehollandiae *Australian darter*

One of Darwin's finches on a large cactus. In the central Galapagos Islands there are about 10 species. This one, **Camarhynchus pallidus,** has the unique habit of using cactus spines or small twigs to probe insects out of crevices and holes when hunting for food.

Darwin's finches

In 1835, Charles Darwin visited the Galapagos Islands during his tour of South America on HMS Beagle and these finches, now named after him, gave him one of the main sources of inspiration for his theory of evolution by natural selection. The ancestors of the finches had presumably been blown to the island by high winds, and once established they were able to evolve into several distinct forms, to take advantage of the different ways of life, or ecological niches available on the islands. The divergence from the ancestral finch to the several modern forms can be seen in many aspects of their lives and it is impossible to discuss even their bodily form without touching on Darwin's all-important theory.

Darwin's finches are a family living on the Galapagos Islands, and nowhere else, except for one species on Cocos Island some 600 miles to the northeast. They are presumed to have originated from now extinct finches on the mainland of South America, 600 miles eastward.

In appearance, they are very drab and unprepossessing—greyish-brown with occasional patches of black on some males, and of the 14 species there is very little variation except in the bills. This is unusual, as on the mainland masses, finches usually differ in plumage and not in body form.

Food fits the bill

The bills are the key to the interest of Darwin's finches. They range from slender to stout and are adapted for eating different kinds of food. This is how the finches have come to live in different ecological niches. There are few species of birds on the Galapagos, so the immigrant ancestors of the finches found little competition and were able to invade these niches. In the process they developed habits similar to those birds that fill the same kinds of niche on the mainland. So, on the Galapagos, there are warbler-finches and woodpecker-finches, and others that are parrot-like, tit-like and so on. None has taken to water, the nearest being one that searches for small crustaceans on the seashore. Neither have

any become regular flesh-eaters, except that one species with a sharp bill has been seen to go to a nesting booby, puncture its skin and drink its blood. It has also been seen to eat gulls' eggs and the half digested fish that boobies feed to their young.

Some Darwin's finches, the ground finches, have stout bills like the bullfinch (p 302) and use them for cracking seeds, but they eat fruit, flowers and caterpillars as well. These finches are most like other finches, which as a family are seed-eaters. Within this group there is a graduation of bill sizes, the size of the bill determining the food taken, as in crossbills. Another finch very closely related to these, but with a longer and sharper bill, lives on the ground.

Probing with a cactus spine

Another group, the tree finches, have pointed bills and behave like tits, hopping agilely among twigs, sometimes hanging upside-down, while investigating bark and leaves for beetles and other small insects. Also searching for insects in the trees is the most remarkable woodpecker-finch, which climbs, woodpecker-like, up and down trees, digging holes in search of food. Having found their quarry, true wood-

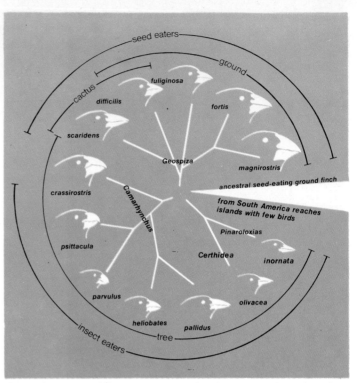

The evolution of finches in the Galapagos Islands. The ancestors of the finches diverged into several different forms to take advantage of the ecological niches available on the islands. The closely related species which evolved differ most markedly in the beak, which has changed shape to become adapted to eat a certain type of food (see diagram above). They differ slightly from each other in body size, and in the shade and streaking of the female plumage, and in the amount of black in the male plumage, but the overall shape is similar to the female small ground finch seen above.

peckers insert a long tongue into the hole to fish the insect out. Woodpecker-finches do not have a long tongue. Instead, they snap off a twig or cactus spine and holding it in the bill, use it to extract the insect. This is a quite astonishing example of tool-using, which is very rare among birds. One other example is of the bower birds using a paintbrush (p 276). Instead of a long tongue being evolved to get their food, these finches have evolved this remarkable piece of behaviour. Furthermore, they also lay up stores of cactus spines for future use.

Among the other special feeding habits of Darwin's finches, there is the parrot-like feeding on soft fruit and pulp of prickly pears by some of the seed-eaters, and the insect-hunting of the warbler-finch. The latter hunts for small insects, sometimes catching them in the air in the manner of a warbler. It even has the warbler-like habit of continually flicking its wings.

Bills for identification

In contrast with the wide variation in feeding habits, the nesting habits of Darwin's finches are very alike. Their nests are built the same height above ground, between 3 and 30 ft, and are very similar in construction. They are bulky, made of twigs, grasses, lichens and so on, with domed roofs to protect the brood from the tropical sun.

During the breeding season, at the same time as the rainy season, the finches defend territories against birds of their own species. They often attack other species, finding their error only when they come close, for the plumages of the different species are very similar and it is not surprising to find that the bills are used as recognition marks.

Mates are attracted by a not very melo-

dious song and by displays that usually take place around the nest. The usual clutch is of 4 white eggs with pink spots. These are incubated for 12 days by the female, which is fed by the male.

Very few enemies

The only enemies Darwin's finches need fear, except domestic cats, are the Galapagos short-eared owl and Galapagos hawk. On some islands the owl rarely takes any, but on others it kills them regularly. The hawk catches only the occasional fledgling.

Darwin's finches are very tame towards humans and fail to recognise cats as being dangerous. On Indefatigable, one of the Galapagos Islands, cats were probably the cause of the extinction of one of the ground-living finches.

Darwin's inspiration

In this discussion it has been possible to describe only some of the variations in form and habit found among Darwin's finches without the story becoming too complicated. It has not been possible, for instance, to show how one species of finch varies in plumage, size or feeding habits from one island to another, or to show how some finches have taken to living on open ground and others in trees. Enough has been said, however, to demonstrate how the ancestral finch has evolved into the different types. This is called adaptive radiation; adaptive because the changes suit each type to a particular way of life. The changes are moulded by certain forces which Darwin realised were vital in the evolution of species. For a population of animals to evolve they must be isolated from their fellows. This occurred in the Galapagos

because once the finches had arrived they no longer mixed with birds from the mainland. They were then free to follow an independent course, in the same way as human cultures evolve independently in isolation.

The boundary between forest and plain can be as much a barrier to the movement of an animal as a wide stretch of water. On the Galapagos Islands, isolation has taken two forms. There is geographical isolation between islands, especially between those widely separated, and there is isolation of habitat. Once away from the rest of the population, various factors will affect the survival of a group of animals. These factors will vary according to the habitat, so one group of animals will evolve along different lines from another. This is how the different Darwin's finches have formed. In the Galapagos Islands predators have not been very important, and it is the feeding methods that have altered so that the different finches have made the best use of available food sources and have reduced competition between each other by specialising in a particular source. The reason why they have had so many sources available to them is that, as is usual on islands, there are not many kinds of animals there, and they did not have to compete with woodpeckers, tits, warblers and the like.

class	**Aves**
order	**Passeriformes**
family	**Fringillidae**
genera	***Geospiza***
	Camarhynchus
	Certhidea
	Pinaroloxias

The dasyure or native cat of Australia: weasel-like with a pointed muzzle, brown-furred with bold white spots.

Dasyure

There are 5 species of dasyures, the native cat of Australia, Tasmania and New Guinea. They are not true cats but carnivorous marsupials, which, together with the Tasmanian devil, make up the subfamily Dasyurinae, although one of them is called a tiger cat. At one time they were placed in a single genus **Dasyurus***, but are now separated as they differ markedly from one another. In form they are more like a civet than a cat. Their legs are short and their tails long and fairly bushy. The coat is white-spotted. The head of some dasyures is almost mouse-like with a pointed muzzle and long whiskers.*

Dasyures are, in fact, related to the marsupial mice, which are no more mice than the dasyures are cats, although similar in appearance.

The eastern native cat or 'quoll', an aborigine name, is one of the best known dasyures. It is about the size of a domestic cat, and occurs in two colour phases. Some quolls are black with large white spots, and others are greyish-brown with creamy-white spots. The latter is more common but both may occur in one litter. Other dasyures have similar colouring, but range from half to twice the quoll's size.

Enemy of poultry farmers

Although generally shy animals, dasyures can be very fierce when cornered. If brought to bay, a tiger cat turns on its enemies, growling, hissing through its nose and sometimes leaping to attack. On the other hand, dasyures can be quite easily tamed.

Some of the dasyures were at one time common animals of the Australian countryside, but now they are extinct in many parts of their former ranges and rare elsewhere. Being flesh-eaters, they are not tolerated by poultry farmers. The western native cat, for instance, is now very much restricted to inland areas. It seems to have adapted itself to the advance of civilisation which has been the downfall of so many animals and has been known to breed in the roofs of houses. It is killed, however, whenever possible by poultry farmers.

Nevertheless, it is possibly unfair to blame man for all the dasyures' misfortunes. Many scientists believe that an epidemic between 1901 and 1903 that hit many marsupials,

Dasyure at home. They lie up during the day in caves, among rocks, or in hollow logs, emerging at night to hunt. Noted for their cautious stalking, they kill by biting at the back of the victim's neck.

Russ Kinne: Photo Res

wiping out some populations, struck the quoll and tiger cat. One zoologist, Calaby, has said, however, that 'no evidence of disease, either observational or clinical, was ever brought forward'. Either way there are only a few scattered remnants of the quoll in Victoria and Tasmania, although it is still quite common around Sydney.

The little northern native cat is still quite common. It lives in northern Australia in rocky places or on wooded plains, where it shelters in crevices or hollow logs. It is found in abandoned houses, where old cast-iron stoves are said to be its favourite nesting place, and even in wrecked ships. A closely related species lives in New Guinea.

Dasyures are mainly tree-dwellers, the exceptions being the quoll and the western native cat, although these can climb well. The others have roughened pads on their feet, giving them a good grip on tree trunks and branches. The tiger cat is so at home in the trees that it can run out to the very tips of branches.

Stealthy carnivores

The dasyures feed on small animals, mainly insects, snails, lizards and small mammals such as rats, mice and young rabbits. When living near rivers they are partial to fish. They also rob nests of eggs and young birds. By eating rodents and rabbits the dasyures are helping to make up for some of the damage they do to poultry, when one das-

yure may attack and kill all the hens in one run in a night.

The name 'native cat' is earned by their cautious stalking. The quoll carefully approaches its prey, then leaps and kills it with a bite at the back of the neck. The larger tiger cat can kill small wallabies and large birds, but its food is usually smaller mammals, birds and reptiles. One was seen stalking a heron, pausing while the heron had its head raised, then rushing forward when the heron lowered its head to search for food, until it was near enough to spring.

Too many babies

Dasyures breed in about May or June, the mechanism of birth being similar to that of other marsupials, which will be described in detail under Kangaroo. The newborn young are minute, only about $\frac{1}{4}$ in. long in an adult tiger cat, growing to $3\frac{1}{2}$ ft from nose to tail tip. They become attached to teats enclosed by a simple pouch, often little more than a fold of skin. When 4 weeks old the baby tiger cats are still only $1\frac{1}{2}$ in. long, but they leave the teats at 7 weeks and are one third grown by 18 weeks, when they become independent.

The teats number 6—8 in the different species of dasyure, and usually there are the same number, or fewer, young; but quoll females have been recorded as bearing up to 24 young. As each female has 6 or possibly 8 teats, most of the litter must die.

'Native tiger' legend

Every so often, reports crop up in the Press of an unknown animal, usually large and often terrifying. They are usually seen for a fleeting second and never leave any more concrete evidence than footprints or the remains of prey. Sometimes the unknown animal captures the public's imagination, like the perennial Loch Ness monster, and scientists are criticized for refusing to acknowledge it. Yet no animal can be accepted into the scientific catalogue of animals until a specimen resides in a museum. The complete body is not necessary; all that is needed is enough to be compared with any other specimens brought in, and to enable those who classify animals to put the species in its right place in the animal kingdom.

One animal known only from reports is the native tiger, reported at intervals in the rocky country and thick forests of northern Queensland, where it is said to prey on calves and kangaroos. It is apparently well-known to the aborigines, and the Europeans who have seen it describe it as being the size of a dingo, like a 'cat just growing into a tiger'. It is said to have transverse black stripes from the shoulders to the root of the long tail. The description also fits the thylacine, or Tasmanian wolf, presumed extinct on the mainland of Australia, but the native tiger is said to have a cat-like face whereas the head of a thylacine is dog-like.

The identity of the native cat was nearly settled when one was shot. Unfortunately the body was eaten by wild pigs and the skin went bad.

As always, the chances of a strange animal surviving without concrete traces being found are slender and so the matter becomes a subject of debate. Those who prefer to believe in the reality of these unknown animals point out that the gorilla was unknown to western science until 1847, the okapi until 1901 and the golden takin of western China until 1910. But these animals lived in areas hardly penetrated by western man. Moreover, they were well-known to the native peoples. Now that travel is easier and few parts of the world remain unexplored, it is harder for a large animal to escape detection, yet there are still animals that successfully elude the scientist for long periods. The Australian marsupials provide three good examples. A burramys, previously known only from fossils, was found in 1966, 130 miles from Melbourne; three dibblers, which had not been seen for 80 years or more, were found the same year in western Australia; and in 1960 a thylacine was reported to have been seen for the first time since one was shot in 1930.

class	**Mammalia**		
order	**Marsupialia**		
family	**Dasyuridae**		
genera & species	***Dasyurus quoll*** *quoll*		
	Dasyurinus geoffroyi *western native cat*		
	Satanellus hallucatus *little northern native cat*		
	Dasyurops maculatus *tiger cat*		

Strange survivors

Three living examples of how hard it is to proclaim an animal extinct:
▷ Until 1966 the burramys was believed extinct, known only from fossils—until found a mere 130 miles from Melbourne. ▽ The dibbler also put in an appearance in 1966 after not being seen for 80 years. Bottom: The rare, dog-faced thylacine bolstered the 'native tiger' legend.

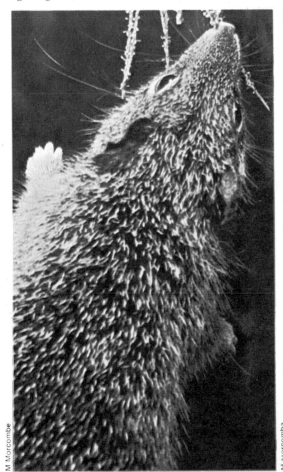

M Morcombe

M Morcombe

Zool. Soc. London

Dead man's fingers

*Dead man's fingers, sometimes called sea-fingers, is better known to zoologists under its scientific name **Alcyonium**. It grows in colonies of polyps, each colony a tough jelly-like mass coloured white or pink to orange and made up of a central mass from which spring thick finger-like lobes. The number of lobes varies but sometimes a colony has 4–5 'fingers', is the size of a man's fist and a pale flesh colour. Such colonies are responsible for the common name.*

*Each colony contains many polyps, each one like a miniature sea-anemone except that the tentacles number eight, have side branches and so are feather-like. The mesenteries dividing the central cavity also number eight. Instead of the hard and continuous stony skeleton of a true coral, **Alcyonium** has a skeleton of separate spicules (literally, little spikes) made of calcium carbonate (chalk). These spicules are more or less needle-shaped and ornamented with knobs and spikes.*

Size depends on depth

The name dead man's fingers or dead man's toes has been used by fishermen for more than 200 years.

John Ellis, the celebrated English naturalist, in his *Natural History of the Corallines* (1755), tells us that they often brought it up in their nets when fishing for flatfish. The colonies usually grow on a pebble or a bivalve shell and the size depends on depth. In waters of 45–60 ft they are usually 1½–2 in. long, in 60–90 ft, 3–4 in. long, measured when they are contracted. Under water they expand, taking in water and swelling. The polyps also expand so instead of 'dead man's fingers' they resemble miniature flower clumps when covered with delicate 8-rayed polyps.

The reason for the differences in size is that in shallower waters there is more wave and current action. At a certain size the colonies tend to be overturned, become buried in silt and die. In sheltered places among rocks, or on pier piles, they can grow bigger and large specimens can sometimes be seen uncovered at extreme low spring tides.

Share and share alike

The tentacles of each polyp trap small swimming animals, paralyse them with their stinging cells, and pass them on to the mouth, as in anemones. The body of the colony is honeycombed with a system of tubes which connects each polyp with the rest. Food caught by one is therefore shared with the rest, so a colony can flourish so long as enough polyps catch food. It is not necessary for all to be feeding all the time.

Growth by budding

Like reef corals dead man's fingers reproduce by free-swimming larvae and by budding from mature polyps. The free-swimming larva is oval, its body covered with cilia which by their united beating drive it along. When a larva settles it changes into a polyp, and the colony is formed from this. A bud appears on its side which grows into a mature polyp, still attached to the parent. Repeated budding forms a colony.

Semi-precious corals

Polyp colonies related to dead man's fingers are especially common on coral reefs in the Indian Ocean and the nearby Pacific waters. Wide areas of the reefs are often covered with them, looking like masses of dull-green or brown fleshy seaweed. A more elegant relative is the organ pipe coral. In this the spicules become closely knitted

GS Giacomelli

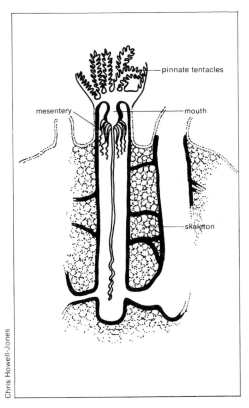

pinnate tentacles

mesentery

mouth

skeleton

Chris Howell-Jones

Kendall McDonald

△ *Section through a dead man's finger polyp shows how each mouth leads into a system of tubes which shares out the food between all polyps. Left and top right: Colonies range in colour from pink or orange to white, resembling miniature flower clumps when feeding. ▷ Like a leprous hand:* **Alcyonium digitatum** *is found in deep coastal water in warm and temperate seas.*

together and they form walls of vertical tubes connected by platforms of the same material. Each tube contains a lilac-tinted polyp and the skeleton as a whole is covered by a skin joining the polyps together. Portions of the skeleton of the organ pipe coral were once treasured as curios and earlier in the century were a familiar sight in parlours and the windows of junk shops.

There is a blue coral also, in which the spicules are joined into a solid mass, but the most famous of the semi-precious corals is the red coral of the Mediterranean. This forms branching tree-like colonies bearing flower-like polyps. The branches are hard, made of spicules cemented together with a chalky mortar and ruby red in colour. This is the red coral of commerce, used for beads and various items of jewellery. In the early years of this century there was a flourishing red coral fishery especially in the Mediterranean, Red Sea and Persian Gulf. The coral lives at depths of 10−600 ft, and in the deeper waters it was fished with a dredge of heavy timber to which a net was attached. The jewellery was largely made in Italy.

phylum	**Coelenterata**
class	**Anthozoa**
order	**Alcyonacea**
genera & species	***Alcyonium digitatum*** *dead man's fingers* ***Corallium rubrum*** *red coral others*

Popperfoto

Deep-sea anglerfish

The deep-sea angler lures its prey into its gaping mouth with a movable, glowing lure which grows from its head. It differs from other anglerfishes (see p 52) in a variety of ways, but notably in having no pelvic fins and in living in midwater instead of on the bottom. It is most abundant at depths of 6 000 ft. There is, moreover, a great difference in size between the sexes, in some species the female being many thousand times the size of the male, who is parasitic on the female. The first ray of the dorsal fin has moved forward onto the head, as in shallow-water anglers, and has been converted into a kind of fishing rod. But in deep-sea anglers only the females have this rod and it has a light at the end to serve as a lure.

Because of the marked differences between the shallow-water and deep-sea anglerfishes they are placed in different suborders. The suborder containing the deep-sea species is subdivided into 10 families, the members of these families being similar in form and habits but differing in such details as length of rod, shape of lure and size of fins.

*Although they live at great depths our first knowledge of the existence of deep-sea anglerfishes came from a specimen washed ashore on the west coast of Greenland a little over a century ago. It was found by Lieutenant-Commander C. Holbøll of the Royal Danish Navy, and was named after him **Ceratias holboelli**. It is appropriate to give main attention to this species because it is one of the best known, as well as being the first to come to light, and is widely distributed throughout the oceans. The female of this species is 3½ ft long, black and with a roughened skin. Her body is pear-shaped, with a large head and gaping mouth. Except for the tail fin, all fins are small, the dorsal and anal fins having strong spines with a thin tissue between the spines. The tail fin is on the same pattern, with long strong spines and a thin membrane between them. The shape of the body and of the fins leaves little doubt that this deep-sea anglerfish does not move about much, but hangs suspended in midwater.*

The compleat angler

Some deep-sea anglers have movable lures. When not in use that of, for example, *C. holboelli* can be drawn backwards into a groove running along the fish's head and back. Although it has not been possible to watch a live fish it seems likely that *C. holboelli* can 'play' its prey, possibly waving its light slightly to attract a smaller fish, then withdrawing the rod slowly into the groove, enticing the prey nearer and nearer to the anglerfish's gaping mouth.

The prey, judged by the stomach contents of the anglerfishes brought up in nets, is smaller fishes, deep-sea prawns and deep-sea euphausians, relatives of the prawn-like krill on which the blue whale feeds.

Parasite husbands, deep-sea style

The most extraordinary feature of all the deep-sea anglerfishes related to *Ceratias* is their method of reproduction. The males are free-swimming at first, with large eyes, no rod or lure, and no digestive tube. Their skin is smooth. The largest found was only ⅔ in. long. In due course the male meets a mature female and grips her skin with his teeth. From this moment he begins to degenerate. His eyes grow smaller and are eventually lost. His skin becomes spiny and around his jaws it fuses with the female's skin leaving a small hole each side of the mouth through which water is drawn for breathing. His blood vessels join with those of the female and he is fed from her blood circulating through his body. This is a kind of placental feeding, like the unborn baby being fed by the mother's blood circulating through the placenta. Meanwhile the male

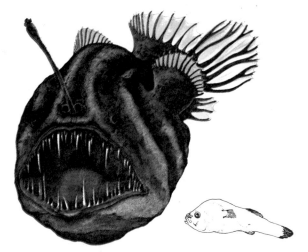

Chris Howell-Jones

grows in size and may reach 6 in. long and internally he grows large testes, the male reproductive organs.

CP Idyll, the American scientist, in his book *Abyss,* has pointed out that the largest-known female of *C. holboelli* was half a million times as heavy as the smallest-known male. One female 40 in. long caught off Iceland had a male 4 in. long attached to her. Another female 2½ in. long had a male ⅔ in. attached to her.

In the North Atlantic spawning takes place in summer, possibly in deep water, but it seems that fertilised eggs must float upwards during development since the very small fry, ⅛ in. long, are found in surface waters. These feed mainly on copepods. The females at this early stage differ from the males in having a well-developed intestinal tract and the beginnings of a rod, between the eyes.

By the time the male is ⅛ in. long he has grown the special teeth on the snout and lower jaw, used to grip the female's skin. He is also slimmer.

While these changes are taking place, males and females are slowly going down to greater depths. Their colour also, is changing to black all over. At first the bodies of the larvae are rounded, almost spherical, inflated by a jelly-like tissue under the skin which probably gives them buoyancy. As growth of the larvae proceeds, this tissue is gradually lost, and since the fishes have no swim-bladder, it is probably the loss of the jelly layer that causes them to descend into deep water.

The mating problem

The light in the lure of the female deep-sea anglerfish is probably under her control. Dr E Bertelsen, the Danish zoologist, has suggested that the luminous bacteria in the cavity of the 'lamp' flash when supplied with extra oxygen. Blood vessels run into this cavity and if the flow of blood were increased, the bacteria would light up and their light fade as blood was withdrawn. It would be very like blushing and growing pale, except that the change is shown by the bacteria.

The light-organs carried by deep-sea animals give out light that may be orange, yellow, yellow-green or blue-green. Dr JAC

Male and female deep-sea anglers (female at left) **Melanocetus johnsoni.** *The diminutive male does not have the movable, luminous 'rod', and he is parasitic on the female. Deep-sea anglers have no pelvic fins; their shape means that they probably hang suspended in midwater and do not move about much, while their black skin absorbs the bluish light which filters down to their level, rendering them invisible in the gloom of the deeps.*

Nicol found that the red surfaces of deep-sea prawns and the black surfaces of deep-sea anglerfishes reflect very little blue light. This means that if the other animals, the fishes and prawns living at these depths, are giving out bluish lights, the black skin of the anglerfishes will render them invisible in the gloom, by absorbing any bluish light.

This may hide them from enemies, but it poses the problem of how the males find the females. It is suggested that flaps and frills of skin that decorate various parts of the female's body, and which differ from one species to another, help the male to recognize a mate of his own kind. Without some method of this kind there would be much frustration in the depths of the ocean.

class	**Pisces**
order	**Lophiiformes**
family	**Ceratiidae**
genus & species	*Ceratias holboelli others*

Jane Burton: Photo Res

Deer mouse

Meal among the toadstools: a deer mouse strikes a Disneylike pose while taking a snack.

Deer mice are American, very similar to the European long-tailed fieldmouse, both in appearance and in habits, but the two belong to different families. There are 55 species, varying in colour from sandy or grey to dark brown. Some are almost white and others nearly black, but in general those living in woods are *darkish, and those living in open or arid country are pale. The underparts and feet are white, hence the alternative name of white-footed mouse. A deer mouse measures 5—15 in. from nose to tip of tail, the tail varying from 1½—8 in. in different species.*

They are found over most of North America, from Alaska and Labrador *southwards, and one species extends into South America, reaching the extreme north of Colombia. They inhabit many kinds of country from swamps and forests to arid, almost desert, country, but each species usually has only a limited habitat and consequently is found only in a relatively small part of the total deer mouse range.*

△ *The wide-eyed face of innocence. Eyes, ears and whiskers all on the alert.*

Litters of deer mice can be found from spring to autumn but more are born in spring and autumn than during the summer, and if the winter is mild, breeding will continue through it. Females begin breeding at 7 weeks, only a few weeks after leaving their mothers, and have up to 4 litters a year.

Many nocturnal enemies

Most deer mice live less than two years, and many never reach maturity but provide food for the many predators that hunt at night. Foxes, weasels, coyotes, bobcats, owls and snakes, all feed on deer mice, and even shrews will occasionally eat them.

Racial 'segregation'

Although similar, the 55 different deer mice can easily be told apart by the specialist in classification, and, one must presume, by the mice themselves. Otherwise they would mix and interbreed and their differences would disappear, especially when different kinds live in the same habitat. Experiments by an American scientist using a Rocky Mountain deer mouse and a Florida deer mouse, which are closely related, showed how the deer mice are segregated.

Special cages were made, each with two side compartments. In preparation for the experiment a Rocky Mountain mouse was put in one compartment and a Florida mouse in the other, and this was repeated for all the cages. After these had remained long enough to impart their smell to the compartments they were taken out. Now, into each cage were put either a Rocky Mountain mouse or a Florida mouse, and these naturally made full use of the available space, including wandering into each compartment. By timing the period each mouse spent in each of the two side compartments of its cage the scientist found that in all cases the test mouse was very obviously drawn to that compartment which carried the smell of its own species. This almost certainly is how mice of the same species, even when sharing a habitat with another species, would be drawn together to breed, for it was noticed that males reacted particularly strongly to the smell of females of their own species on heat. So although it may sometimes appear that there are mixed populations of deer mice, the different species are really living separately.

There was, however, one difference between the Rocky Mountain mice and the Florida mice: the latter were much more likely to spend time in compartments smelling of Rocky Mountain mice. The reason for this seems to be that in Florida there is only one species of deer mouse, and discrimination is no longer necessary; but in the west there are many species and if their strains are to be kept pure, they must be able to distinguish between their own fellows and those of closely related species.

▷ *Deermouse drying itself.*

Overlapping territories

Deer mice are nocturnal, coming out during the day only if they are very hungry, or if there is a cover of snow that allows them to forage under its shelter. During the evening they can be heard trilling or buzzing, a noise quite unlike the squeaks of other mice, and in some parts of the United States this has led to their being called vesper mice. They also drum with the front feet when excited.

Each deer mouse has a home range which it covers regularly in search of food. The extent of the range varies considerably and depends on the amount of food available. In the grasslands of south Michigan the average size of the ranges of male deer mice is ⅗ of an acre, while those of the females are slightly smaller. The home range of a mammal is not strictly comparable with the territory of a bird. Only a few birds keep a territory all through the year, but more important, a mammal does not defend its range so vigorously. The borders of neighbouring ranges overlap, sometimes considerably, and the ranges of two females may be almost identical, but it is only the inner parts of the territory around the nest that will be defended vigorously.

Within its range, a deer mouse may have several refuges in abandoned burrows or birds' nests, under logs or in crevices. Sometimes a deer mouse will come indoors and make its nest in an attic or storage room. Each nest is used for a short time, being abandoned when it becomes soiled, for deer mice limit hygiene to cleaning their fur.

Burrows with a bolt hole

The nest is an untidy mass of grass and leaves, lined with moss, fine grass or feathers. Sometimes the deer mice make their own burrows. The Oldfield mouse, a species of deer mouse living in Alabama and Florida, makes a burrow leading down to a nest which is 1 ft underground. Then from the other side another burrow leads up again but stops just short of the surface. This presumably serves as a bolt hole in case a snake or other narrow-bodied enemy finds its way in. A traditional way of catching these mice is to push a pliable switch or wand down the hole, twiddle it about until it can be pushed up the escape burrow, and catch the mouse as it breaks out.

Are they a pest?

Seeds and berries are the main food of deer mice but they also eat many insects such as beetles, moths and grasshoppers, which are chased and bitten or beaten to death. Insect larvae, snails and slugs are devoured, and deer mice also eat carrion such as dead birds and mammals, and they will gnaw cast antlers.

Deer mice are something of a problem in plantations or on farms, where they eat seeds of new-sown crops, which they smell out and dig up. But even when abundant, they are not as much of a pest as meadow voles and other small rodents. To even the score, deer mice are helpful because they eat chafer grubs that damage the roots of young trees.

Hanging on to mother

In spring the males search for mates, perhaps finding females whose ranges overlap theirs. At first their advances are repulsed but the males eventually move into the females' nests, staying there for a few days only but sometimes, it is thought, forming permanent pairs.

The female gives birth to a litter of 1–9 young after 3 or 4 weeks. At birth the young mice are blind, deaf, and apart from their whiskers, naked. They hang firmly to their mother's teats and she can walk around with them trailing behind. If the nest is disturbed she will drag them in this manner to a new site. Any baby that does fall off is picked up and carried in its mother's mouth.

class	**Mammalia**
order	**Rodentia**
family	**Cricetidae**
genus & species	*Peromyscus maniculatus* *others*

Desman

Desmans are aquatic mammals of the same family as the moles, having the mobile, continually probing snout and small eyes typical of moles and shrews. The scaly tail is long, equal to the head and body length of 7 — 8 in., and flattened from side to side. Running the length of the tail is a ridge of hairs increasing its efficiency as a propeller. Desmans swim with a side-to-side motion of the tail helped by the feet. Their hindfeet are webbed with stiff hairs bordering the outside toes, making a larger paddle. The front feet also have fringes of hair but are only partly webbed. Often all that is seen of a desman is its long snout showing above water as it swims. Pyrenean and Russian desmans are very similar and are the survivors of a population that once ranged across Europe, including the British Isles.

The Russian desman, the best known of the two, now lives in the river basins of the Ural, Kama, Volga and Don, together with small rivers flowing into the Sea of Azov. It is found in the slower-running parts of the rivers and in lakes and pools such as swampy oxbow pools formed where the river has changed course. The Pyrenean desman is found in faster-flowing streams in northern Spain and Portugal, and in the southern borders of France.

Underwater runways

Desmans live in burrows, coming out to feed at night. The burrows are dug in the banks of rivers and pools, and lead to nest cavities just under the surface of the ground, usually beneath a log or boulder or among the roots of a bush. Because the nest is near the surface, it is ventilated by air filtering down through the soil, while the log, boulder or bush protects the nest from possible destruction by a large animal putting its foot through the roof. Also, in winter, such protection will ensure that there will not be such a depth of snow as to blanket off the air supply.

The burrow leads from the nest to the water, opening well under the surface, so the entrance is not blocked by ice in winter. The length of the burrow depends on the slope of the bank; short if it is steep, long if it gently shelves to the water's edge. The nest is built above the normal water level but it may be flooded in spring, when the desmans have to flee to higher ground and make temporary nests. Sometimes, however, the floods come before the ice has melted and the desmans are trapped. It has been known for them to be exterminated in some places when the ice has persisted during the spring floods.

If a burrow is occupied, there is a litter of fish bones at the entrance to the burrow, and a clear channel through the bed of the river or pool leading away from the entrance of the burrow. There is also a musky odour from scent glands at the base of the desman's tail. If debris has lodged in the

channel it means that the burrow is abandoned, for desmans are very much creatures of habit and have runways or trenches leading from their burrows and through the shallows, which they use as regularly as a mole uses its tunnels.

Insect eaters

Like all mammals classed as insectivores, such as moles, shrews and hedgehogs, desmans are voracious. They eat small freshwater animals: crustaceans, snails, insect

larvae, leeches and worms, together with frogs and fish. The Pyrenean desman also hunts on land, searching for insects among the vegetation on the banks, but its mainstay is freshwater amphipods (see p 36).

Obscure breeding habits

Very little is known about the breeding habits of desmans, and considering their underground and underwater life, it would be very difficult to make a study of courtship and care of the young. The mating season is known, from an examination of freshly-killed desmans, to run from January to May in the Pyrenees, and is probably the same in Russia. There are 1—5, perhaps more, young. Judging by other insectivores, it is unlikely that the male plays any part in raising the family.

Infested by beetles

Desmans are known to be eaten by ospreys, kites and harriers, and are no doubt preyed upon by flesh-eating mammals and large fish. They have also been found with their fur crawling with small beetles. These beetles are parasites living in the fur and are similar to beetles that have been found on beavers.

The lure of the fur

During this century there has been a market for the soft, mole-like, reddish fur of the desmans but it is only in Russia that they have been trapped or shot extensively. Shooting an animal that lives underground

or underwater is not easy. The method used is to hunt desmans from canoes. One man paddles while another sits in the bows with a gun. When a line of bubbles from a submerged desman is sighted, the hunter follows it with his gun and fires as the desman surfaces to breathe.

Trapping is easy by comparison. A cylindrical trap, about 30 in. long and 10 in. in diameter, with conical sleeves at each end on the lobster pot principle, is placed in the trench at the entrance to the burrow.

*Pyrenean desman **Galemys pyrenaicus**.*

Any desman going in or coming out runs into it and is drowned.

Although desmans have not been as over-exploited as other fur-bearing animals, the Russians have taken measures to conserve them and to introduce them to new areas, such as the basin of the River Dnieper.

class	**Mammalia**
order	**Insectivora**
family	**Talpidae**
genera & species	***Desmana moschata*** *Russian desman* ***Galemys pyrenaicus*** *Pyrenean desman*

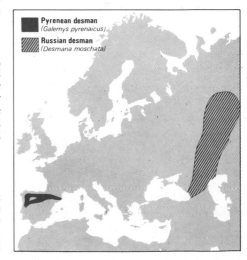

Pyrenean desman
(Galemys pyrenaicus)

Russian desman
(Desmana moschata)

Devil fish

Less than a score of species of devil fish, or devil rays, are known. They are related to skates, rays and sharks and like them have a cartilaginous skeleton. The largest is the manta ray, or greater devil fish, 22 ft across and weighing up to 3 500 lb or more. Cornel Lumière, French skin-diver, records a maximum size of 60 ft across and 5 000 lb weight. The smallest is the pygmy Australian devil ray, only 2 ft across. 'Manta' is Spanish

flying through the water. The devil fish resembles an enormous bat, and has been called sea bat or batfish. Another name is vampire ray. Usually solitary or in pairs, devil fish sometimes form small schools. Normally their movements appear slow and somewhat lazy. At times a devil fish will swim slowly at the surface or turn complete somersaults in the water, or leap high into the air, landing with a tremendous impact.

Large fish, small food
When feeding, a devil fish uses its 'horns' like scoops to fan food towards the enormous mouth as it cruises through water

rich in plankton. Its food includes small crustaceans, young or very small fishes and other members of the plankton, very much as in the other leviathans, the whale shark and basking shark. There is a special lattice-work covering the gills which keeps the food in the mouth until it can be swallowed. Without this the gills would be fatally clogged.

Outsize babies
Devil fish bear their young alive. Mating is

▽ *Head-on approach of a 14ft manta, with its 'horns' folded crossways. Bottom: A skin-diver hitches a ride on an impassive manta.*

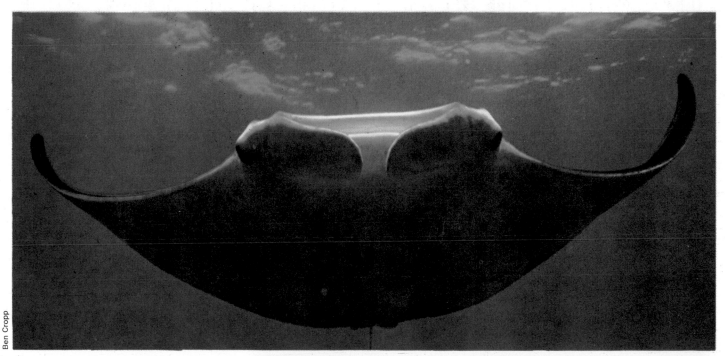

Ben Cropp

for blanket and refers to the widespread shape of the pectoral fins. As in other rays, the body is flattened from above downwards, the pectoral fins are large and triangular. The tail is long and slender and may have a small poison spine. In the related stingrays the spine is large. Many devil fish lack the spine entirely. The mouth is large and at the front of the head whereas in most sharks, skates and rays it is underneath. At each corner of the mouth and directed forwards is a large 'horn' formed from a part of the pectoral fins.

Dr Bernard Heuvelmans, in his book **Monstres marins**, *tells how a South American scholar, Enrique Onffroy de Thoron, on seeing in 1866 a large devil fish from a ship, jumped to the conclusion that it was a living* **Chirotherium**, *a giant amphibian whose fossil remains had been found in 1833 in Thuringia.*

Vampires of the sea
Devil fish live in tropical and subtropical seas. Unlike other rays and skates which live mainly on the seabed, they spend most of their time swimming at or near the surface. They swim with graceful flapping movements of the enormous pectoral fins, as if

Ben Cropp

605

Undersea bomber stream: a shoal of smoothtail mantas in the Gulf of California.

carried out by the two partners coming together, their undersides facing, the female curving her pectoral fins upwards to embrace those of the male. The male has a pair of organs, known as claspers, which are in fact intromittent organs used alternately to convey the sperms into the female's oviduct. Usually there is only one young at birth but it is well-developed and large. One female 15 ft across contained an embryo 5 ft across which weighed 20 lb.

A classic gentle giant

Old beliefs among pearl-divers include the notion that these flattened giants would cover them with their vast wings and, holding them, would devour them. A devil fish's teeth are very small and flattened, and the giant manta has teeth in the lower jaw only. It was also a belief among seamen that a devil fish could seize an anchor and tow a vessel away.

Probably three things, over and above their large size, have added colour to such notions. One is that a manta can be dangerous, inadvertently, by smashing or capsizing a small boat with a blow of its pectoral fin, especially if it lands on the boat following a leap. Secondly, a harpooned manta will tow a fair-sized vessel, and it can take enormous punishment from harpoon, lance and gunshot before succumbing.

A third thing must be the tremendous

noise it makes on returning to water after a leap. JR Norman, in his *History of Fishes*, quotes a Mr Holder for an account of a jumping devil fish: 'There came out of the darkness, near at hand, a rushing swishing noise; then a clap as of thunder, which seemed to go roaring and reverberating over the reef, like the discharge of a cannon'—a noise that can be heard several miles away.

Because of their large size it has not been possible to study closely the habits of devil fish. Nevertheless, with the advent of skin-diving enough has been gleaned to confirm what was already suspected by scientists half a century ago, that devil fish are not as black as they are painted. They seem to have excellent sight and an overwhelming sense of curiosity, and skin-divers tell of giant mantas swimming elegantly to within 6 ft to examine them.

Cornel Lumière has described devil fish as no more dangerous to the skin-diver than a litter of puppies.

class	**Selachii**
order	**Batoidei**
family	**Mobulidae**
genera & species	*Manta birostris* *Mobula diabolis* *others*

Dhole

The red, or wild, dog of India and south-east Asia is not a true dog although it resembles village or pi-dogs, with which it is sometimes confused in reports. It can be distinguished by rounded ears and a shorter muzzle. In the northern parts of their range dholes have heavy, yellowish to greyish brown coats with dense underfur in winter, turning darker in summer. To the south, the coat is less thick and is yellowish brown all the year. The tail is tipped with black.

The dhole's range covers India (although not Ceylon), southeastern Asia to Indonesia, as well as parts of the USSR, China and Korea.

Roaming in packs

Dholes once lived in packs of 100 or more in forests of both hill and plain. Their numbers are now decreased as the deer and other large mammals on which they feed have become scarce. A pack would remain in one area, sheltering under boulders or in deserted burrows and hunting by day until they had killed so much game that they were forced to move on. Now that muntjac, chital and other deer are becoming so rare, the dholes are often shot to prevent the herds of deer being destroyed completely.

Dholes do not bark but growl or whine. Hunters have decoyed them by blowing across a brass cartridge case to imitate the dhole's peculiar howling whistle, which is apparently a mating call.

Tireless hunters

Like Cape hunting dogs to which they are related, dholes hunt in packs remorselessly running down their quarry. They do not run at any great speed but follow the scent of their prey in a long, loping, tireless canter until it is eventually worn down.

Once within striking distance of the exhausted prey, they attack any part that can be grasped, slashing the flanks and hanging on to the lips, nose or tail. A story very prevalent in India is that they emasculate their prey and reports tell of kills found with the testicles removed, yet it seems that the dholes do not attack any part of the body in particular, but seize any part they can. After the kill, the carcase is eaten at once for dholes will not touch decaying meat.

Although the dholes wreak havoc among deer and are sometimes shot where deer are becoming scarce, under completely natural conditions they play a useful part in the overall balance of nature. They keep the deer moving and prevent their overgrazing the land.

Muntjac, chital and sambur are the main prey of dholes in India, but the packs will attack larger animals, including Indian buffaloes, wild boars and even other carnivores such as Himalayan black bears, and sloth bears. The big cats, such as tigers, cheetahs and leopards take flight after a clash with a pack of dholes perhaps over the ownership of a kill, and they have to take to the trees. If caught, the pack can overwhelm and kill them.

Luckily for the inhabitants of Asia, dholes do not attack man. There is one record of an attack in Indonesia but there is no definite proof that dholes were involved; the attack could well have been made by a pack of feral dogs.

Breeding in communal dens

In India, at least, dholes are born all the year round, but mostly in January and February. After a gestation of about 9 weeks 2—6, perhaps more, young are born. Several females may raise their young in a communal den.

Are they acid-throwers?

A widespread story in Asia is that a pack will urinate on some bushes in a selected part of a wood, then drive their prey through them. As the prey crashes through the bushes, it is blinded by the acid fumes given off by the urine and set upon by the dholes before its eyes have a chance to clear. Another version of the story is that the dholes spray urine straight into the eyes of their prey by flipping it with their tails. To do this while on the run must require considerable gymnastic skill, yet in Burma it was thought that even tigers and elephants could be made helpless and killed in this manner.

With any strange story of animal behaviour it is interesting to speculate as to how it arose. Seemingly impossible stories usually have some basis of fact, which has been distorted by uncritical observation and elaborate embroidery as the story is handed on. The story of the dhole's chemical warfare may perhaps have started as an observation of their marking bushes in the same manner as domestic dogs. The elaboration to splashing urine with their tails is not so easy to explain away. In Europe, however, wolves were credited with the same behaviour, but they were said to have dipped their tails in water from a pool or stream. Perhaps the original versions spoke of urine being used and this may have been changed to make the story acceptable to the prim readers of a later age.

class	**Mammalia**
order	**Carnivora**
family	**Canidae**
genus & species	*Cuon alpinus*

Northern dhole **Cuon alpinus.**

Chris Howell–Jones

Dibatag

The dibatag is a long-necked gazelle-like antelope, also known as Clarke's gazelle. It was not discovered until 1891 and has been seen only intermittently since, although it can be numerous locally. It stands 31—35 in. at the shoulder, weighs 56—70 lb (50—62 in females) and the top of its head is up to 4 ft from the ground. Its coat is greyish-fawn, white on the belly, and there is a white streak on each side of the face ending in a whitish ring around each eye. The muzzle is hairy, the tail a foot or more long and mainly black. When alarmed and running away both neck and tail are carried erect (Somali **dabu** = tail, **tag** = erect). The males only, have horns and these are up to 13 in. long, curving backwards in the lower third then forwards and slightly outwards.

Restricted to parts of Somalia and eastern Ethiopia, the dibatag lives in pairs, in groups of 3—5 or in small family groups of up to 7 in areas hot throughout the year and fairly dry. It keeps mainly to the **durr** grass on open grassy plains with scattered small scrubby bushes and umbrella mimosa (acacia). The dibatag does not seem to have a well-defined home range. It moves from one area to another during different seasons, probably depending on which plants are in leaf.

Shy and well-camouflaged

Knowledge of the dibatag's habits is scanty because the animal is hard to see. Its colour makes it inconspicuous, it keeps near cover or actually in it and its shyness and alert senses make it impossible to approach within 100 yds except when in the open when it seems to be less wary and can be approached to about 50 yds. The *durr* grass, moreover, may be 6 ft tall, completely hiding the 4ft dibatag. When disturbed it moves away unhurriedly, standing for about a minute watching the intruder before trotting nonchalantly away. When resting it lies up in a slight depression in the ground, or in the lee of a bush.

Dibatag feed in the morning and late afternoon, keeping to the shade of a bush or tree during the hot midday. They eat the *durr* grass but they seem to prefer the leaves and flowers of acacia and the leaves of the *Commiphora* shrub. Like the long-necked gerenuk, which it resembles, the dibatag sometimes stands on its hindlegs with the forefeet planted against the trunk of the tree when browsing.

Young parked in a bush

Breeding appears to take place throughout the year but there is a main breeding season during March—May coinciding with the rainy season. There is one young per birth which the mother leaves in a convenient bush returning from time to time to nurse it until it is old enough to follow her.

The dibatag is protected by its natural wariness and by hunting permits being issued with discretion. Nevertheless, there

J Meester

△ *Young dibatag buck from Mogadishu, Somaliland shows its graceful neck and posture.*
▽ *Adult buck, with backward/forward curving horns, which grow up to 13 in.*

A Maynard

is illegal hunting, and dibatag skins can be bought for a few shillings in local shops. A rare animal, its existence is threatened largely because it inhabits a restricted area which is being encroached upon by man.

Known in Ancient Egypt

The other long-necked antelope, the gerenuk of East Africa, was made known to science in 1878 although it had been seen before this by Europeans visiting the region. Even then little attention was paid to it until about a quarter of a century ago since when it was often mentioned in popular natural history. Not uncommonly it is spoken of as an animal well known to the Ancient Egyptians which was portrayed, according to some accounts, on Egyptian sculptures, paintings, bas-reliefs and murals. The truth is the animal in question was portrayed on an antiquity believed to have been part of a ceremonial palette for grinding eye-paint (kohl), dated about 3100 BC.

The story stems from the *Guide to Game Animals* published by the British Museum (Natural History) in 1913. In this it was tentatively suggested that the animal figured on the palette might have been the gerenuk. The greater likelihood is that it was the dibatag, an animal that has been even more overlooked than the gerenuk. There are two grounds for this: the range of the dibatag is north of that of the gerenuk and therefore much nearer the land of the Pharaohs, and the animal depicted bears a much closer resemblance to the dibatag, especially in the proportions of the neck and forelegs.

class	**Mammalia**
order	**Artiodactyla**
family	**Bovidae**
genus & species	*Ammodorcas clarkei*

Dik-dik

Help to the hunted, hindrance to the hunter, the six species of dik-dik are distributed over Africa south of the Sahara. They are named for the call of the female when alarmed, which is variously written as 'zik-zik' and 'dik-dik'. Otherwise both sexes use a shrill whistle. The calls of these small antelopes alert the game in the area of disturbance so hunters regard dik-diks as a great nuisance because they are of little use themselves. They have no worthwhile 'trophies' for the sportsman, their flesh has a musky flavour and because they alert other game they tend to spoil the hunting.

Dik-diks have a 21—27in. head and body length, they stand 12—16 in. at the shoulder and weigh 7—11 lb, the females being larger than the males. Their coat is soft, coloured grey to reddish-brown and grey to white on the underparts. Only the males have horns, short and stout at the base, ringed and longitudinally grooved, and often partly hidden in a tuft of hair on the top of the head. There is a pair of crescent-shaped scent glands on the face, in front of each eye. The tail is a mere stump and characteristic features are the puffy, hairy muzzle and longish snout.

The first dik-dik known to Europeans, in 1816, was the one Arabs called Ben-Israel (sons of Israel). It was named Salt's dik-dik after Sir Henry Salt, the explorer who travelled widely in north-west Africa, especially Abyssinia, in the early years of the 19th century.

▽ Dik-dik youngster; the animal's puffy, snout-like muzzle shape is accentuated in the young fawns. As in most antelopes they walk soon after birth.
▷ In its element. Shy and elusive, dik-diks stand only 12—16 in. at the shoulder and readily take to the undergrowth to hide.

△ *Dik-diks usually live in small groups of 2—3; they favour arid scrub territory and follow regular paths through the undergrowth.*

The hare-like antelope

Dik-diks are shy and elusive, they readily disappear into cover, but if flushed race away with erratic leaps, somewhat like hares, on a more or less zig-zag course. They live solitarily or in pairs, sometimes in small family parties, but the usual number seen together is 2—3. Where there are dense thorn thickets they may gather in larger numbers, but they usually live in dry areas with only scattered brush vegetation, through which they have regular paths.

Feeding at dusk

Dik-diks feed mainly at twilight, grazing or browsing the shrubs and trees. One analysis of their stomach contents, made in a game park, showed they feed on 56% leaves of shrubs, 23% leaves of trees, 17% grass and the rest is made up of herbs and sedges. They have also been seen eating acacia pods knocked down by feeding vervet monkeys. The vegetation is grasped, as in tapirs, by their long mobile snouts. They sometimes frequent the banks of streams, where there is enough drinking water, but in the drier areas they seem to get sufficient water from their food and from dew to be able to go for months without drinking.

Preyed on by pygmies

Nothing is known of mating habits or the gestation period. It is believed the young are born during and at the end of the rainy season. One of Kirk's dik-diks lived in captivity for just over 9 years, but that is all that is known of the life span. There is little information on enemies: presumably medium-sized carnivores of all kinds prey on them. The pygmies of the Ituri Forest in the Congo kill them in large numbers and, according to Ernest P Walker in *Mammals of the World*, sell them by the roadside, slung on poles like rabbits. Elsewhere in Africa dik-diks are not molested by the local people. The Bushmen of Southwest Africa have a superstition about killing them, but what the superstition may be is not recorded. The Bakete tribe, in the Congo, neither kill nor eat them, in the belief that to do so would cause their teeth to fall out.

Gunning them down

In the 1930's, in the Natural History Museum in London, an exhibition was staged of the mammals of the different continents. A fair proportion of the people visiting the exhibition were men who had hunted game especially in Africa. One was overheard to say to his companion that on one trip to Africa he had shot 10 000 dik-diks. On the face of it this seems insensate slaughter but it may have been that he did this to prevent these charming little antelopes from disturbing the larger game he was stalking. It seems also to be a prodigious feat of gunmanship until we read what Richard Lydekker wrote in 1911, that 'two or three may be killed at one shot'.

class	**Mammalia**
order	**Artiodactyla**
family	**Bovidae**
genera & species	*Madoqua saltiana* *Rhynchotragus kirkii, others*

Dingo

The dingo is the wild dog of Australia, about the size of a collie, standing about 20 in. at the shoulder. The ears are erect and pointed and the tail bushy, often with a white tip. It is popularly supposed that dingoes always have the yellow-brown coat immortalised in the Yellow-dog Dingo of Kipling's *Just So Stories*, but they vary from light red to brown and some may be brown with black streaks. Albinos are known and in southeastern Australia there is a whitish breed. The darker dingoes are often assumed to be the offspring of matings with domestic alsatians, but this is not necessarily so, although dingo × dog crosses are quite common.

▽ A dingo family, which can run to 8 pups. Dingoes hunt in family parties, running down their prey in a long, tenacious chase and worrying it until it tires.

◁ *Careful inspection: dingoes check out a dead wallaby before feeding. Natural caution makes dingoes hard to trap with poisoned bait. Above left: Apron strings—dingo bitch with wobbly pup. Adults (above right) often lead family packs to kill scores of sheep and cattle.*

The Aborigines' companion

The animals of Australia are unique because the continent was cut off from the main land mass of Europe, Asia and Africa before the placental, or true, mammals arose, and the marsupial, pouched mammals were able to survive in large numbers. When the Europeans arrived in the 18th century the only true mammals apart from man were bats and rats, which are thought to have floated over from southeast Asia on driftwood, and the dingo. The most likely explanation of the dingo's presence is that it was brought over in one of the Aborigine invasions from Asia as a domestic dog, and later went wild. The New Guinea singing dog is thought to have had the same origin. Remains of dingoes dating back 6 000 years have been found, and present-day Aborigines use them for hunting. They are captured when young, and, if necessary, suckled by the Aborigine women.

Support for this idea lies in the similarity between the dingo and the Asian pariah dogs. They may have both descended from the dhole. Neither the dhole, the dingo nor the singing dog can bark. Instead they howl o whine, the howl of the singing dog being a remarkable yodel that gives the dog its name.

Dingoes have flourished in Australia. Their only competitors were the Tasmanian devil, thylacine and, perhaps, the tiger cat (see dasyure p 617). It is probably the competition with the dingo that caused the Tasmanian devil and the thylacine to become rare and finally extinct on the mainland. Their final stronghold, if they still survive, is Tasmania, which the dingo never reached.

Dingoes live alone or in small family parties. They are found all over Australia and appear to have regular migrations along definite tracks. There is evidence that many dingoes breed in inland parts of Australia and migrate to the coastal strip in winter.

Chasing their prey

Like all dogs, dingoes chase their prey, wearing them out in a long chase, for they are not fast runners. Large animals such as kangaroos, sheep or cattle are chased until the dingoes can catch them, or if there is a number of sheep or cattle they are harassed and chivvied about until the weaker ones drop back. As the prey fails in strength, the dingoes worry it, slashing at its head and legs but keeping clear of the hooves, until it collapses.

Sometimes the dingoes meet their match, as when a kangaroo turns at bay. Leaning back on its tail it can deliver kicks powerful enough to rip open the dingoes' bellies.

Breeding

The male dingo marks its territory with urine, like a domestic dog. It mates in winter and the pups are born in spring, some 9 weeks later. The litter consists of up to 8 pups, which are sheltered in a den where they are suckled for 2 months. After that they stay with their parents for at least a year, and hunt as a pack.

Eagle fodder

Apart from man, and prey brought to bay, dingoes are in danger from crocodiles and snakes in the tropical parts of Australia, and from wedge-tailed eagles. These are the world's largest eagles, and two working together have been seen to kill an adult dingo, but this is exceptional; it is young dingoes and the old or infirm that usually fall prey to them.

A sticky end

Since Europeans began farming in Australia, the dingo has been an ever present problem. Thousands of sheep and cattle are slain each year, a family of dingoes sometimes killing a score or more in one night, apparently out of sheer blood lust, but more likely through the inexperience and excitement of the young dingoes. Consequently, firm steps are taken against them. Thousands of square miles of sheep country have been fenced, at a cost of millions of pounds.

As a result of the bounty thousands of dingoes have been shot or poisoned, but despite a prediction 80 years ago that they would soon become extinct, they are still common, even in fairly well-populated areas. But a greater problem than the ordinary dingo is the rogue, perhaps one that is wounded and so unable to hunt wild prey, or a dingo-collie cross, that makes a speciality of killing sheep. Bounties of over $A200 may be offered for the scalp of such a rogue, and they may be well earned. Ellis Troughton, the distinguished Australian zoologist, tells of a wily rogue that evaded all the efforts of a dogger, as dingo hunters are called, to trap or poison it. Eventually the dogger noticed that the dingo followed regular tracks so he spread a trail of poisoned golden syrup. The dingo, finding his paws becoming sticky, licked them, and succumbed to man's greater cunning.

class	**Mammalia**
order	**Carnivora**
family	**Canidae**
genus & species	**Canis familiaris dingo** *dingo*

Dipper

The dippers, of which there are four very similar species, are starling-sized, wren-like birds with short wings and tails. The common dipper, with brown plumage and white 'bib', is found over most of Europe and in some parts of western Asia. In the British Isles it lives in most places where there are suitable streams, shallow, swift-flowing and with boulders, which is why it is absent from southeast England. In parts of Asia its range overlaps with the brown dipper, but the latter keeps to streams on the lower slopes of mountains. The North American dipper, with a slate-grey body and brown head, lives in the west from Alaska to Panama. In the Andes there is the white-capped dipper.

Well-oiled water birds

Dwelling in clear, fast-flowing streams, the dipper leads a life quite unlike any other bird. It flits about the rocks and boulders, walking and flying in and out of the water and, apparently, walking along the bottom.

Dippers are the only members of the passerines, or perching birds, that lead an aquatic life. Under their plumage is a thick layer of down, and their preen glands are enormous, supplying all the oil needed to keep the plumage waterproof. Dippers have movable flaps over their nostrils and well-developed third eyelids (nictitating membranes) to keep out the spray. Unlike other water birds, however, dippers do not have webbed feet. They have to paddle very rapidly to make headway.

For a long time the dippers' claim to fame was that they were able to walk on the beds of streams, rather than to swim like other water birds. The hippopotamus is another that is supposed to be able to walk underwater. Certainly, a dipper appears to be walking underwater as it runs down a boulder, along the gravel bed and up the side of another rock but, once underwater, it is using its wings to 'fly' through the water, although the feet help. Unlike other diving birds, such as cormorants and divers, dippers are very buoyant and they ought not to be able to stay on the bottom. At one time it was thought that the flow of water over the dipper's back pressed it against the bottom, but it can travel with the current, too.

Apart from running in and out of water, a dipper can also fly in and out, diving in or surfacing and taking off without pausing. The usual duration of a dive is about 10 seconds in 1–2 ft of water, but dippers can stay under for half a minute and have been known to go down 20 ft.

Feeding in the water

Dippers in the British Isles were hard hit by the severe winter of 1962–3, but where the ice is thin and there are plenty of holes, or there is an air space between the water and the ice, then they are able to continue feeding. The bulk of the dipper's food is insect larvae such as caddis flies, dragonflies and stoneflies. Water beetles, crustaceans, worms and molluscs are also eaten and

John Warham

A dipper returns to its nest, sited under the overhang behind a miniature waterfall. Their nests are rarely found far from water, and are often in danger of floods.

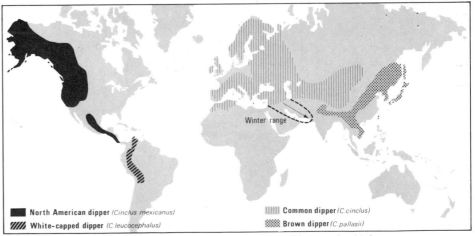

■ **North American dipper** *(Cinclus mexicanus)*
▨ **White-capped dipper** *(C. leucocephalus)*
▥ **Common dipper** *(C. cinclus)*
▦ **Brown dipper** *(C. pallasii)*

Dippers have a worldwide distribution — and lead a life quite unlike any other bird.

dippers can catch minnows and newts. They search either among boulders or along the stream bed. Often a dipper will stand on a submerged boulder and catch small animals as they float past. In fish farms they can be a pest, eating fish eggs and fingerling trout.

River bank nesting

A pair of dippers establishes and guards a territory that consists of a stretch of stream or river about ¼–½ mile long. Neighbouring pairs are usually well spread out with some distance between the edges of the territories.

Nests are made in banks or cliffs overlooking the water or in stone walls, under bridges and among tree roots. Only very rarely are they found at any distance from the water. The nests are cup-shaped, 8–12 in. diameter, made chiefly of moss and intertwined grass, lined with grass and leaves, covered with a roof of moss.

There are usually 5 eggs which are brooded by the female alone, who leaves the nest only occasionally to feed. The eggs hatch in 16 days and the chicks stay in the nest for about 3 weeks.

Dippers will often stand on submerged pebbles or boulders, catching small animals as they drift past on the current.

Devotion to duty

In 1962, James Alder, a Northumberland ornithologist studying dippers, was worried that heavy rain would swell the stream so much that the nests he was watching would be destroyed. At two nests there seemed little hope, for they were built in the bank under an overhanging 'flap' of turf, left behind as the bank underneath had been washed away. The water was up to the level of the overhang but, watching from a safe distance, Alder saw a dipper appear with food in its beak. It landed on the water by the nest and dived under. Seconds later it reappeared, its beak empty, and it went searching for more food. At both nests he watched the parent dippers regularly flying up with food and diving in. Later the rain stopped and the floods subsided. Inspection of the nests showed the water had lapped the nests, but air had been trapped under the overhang and the adults had been able to surface by the nests and feed the young. On another occasion a nest was splashed by a waterfall during floods but the female blocked the nest entrance with her body and kept the eggs dry.

class	**Aves**
order	**Passeriformes**
family	**Cinclidae**
genus & species	***Cinclus cinclus*** *common dipper* ***C. leucocephalus*** *white-capped dipper* ***C. mexicanus*** *North American dipper* ***C. pallasii*** *brown dipper*

Diver

The divers, or loons, are water birds with streamlined bodies, very short tails and straight, pointed bills. Their legs are set well back, like other powerful swimmers such as cormorants, but unlike them the divers have not developed an upright stance on land. Furthermore, their legs are enclosed in the body down to the ankle joint, so divers can only shuffle clumsily a few paces at a time.

Divers are distributed around the higher latitudes in the northern hemisphere. The great northern diver, with its black-and-white spotted body and collar, breeds in most of Canada, extending into the northern parts of the United States, the southern coasts of Greenland, Iceland and Bear Island. In the winter, it migrates south and often visits British coasts. It may have bred in the Shetlands. The white-billed diver resembles the great northern diver except for its whitish-yellow bill. The black-throated and red-throated divers have similar plumage patterns and distribution. The former has black-and-white barrings on its back, dark grey on the head and neck and a black patch on the throat. On the red-throated diver this patch is chestnut and the head and neck are dove grey. Both birds live in northern Canada, Siberia and northern Europe, including Scandinavia and Scotland. The red-throated diver is also found in Greenland, Iceland, the Faeroes, Spitzbergen and other Arctic islands.

In America divers are called loons from the Old Norse **lómr** *or awkward person, in allusion to their shuffling gait on land. In Iceland they are* **lomr** *and in Orkney* **loom.**

Deep diver, powerful swimmer

Divers are powerful swimmers and by expelling air from their bodies and plumage, they can swim with only head and neck showing, or they may even submerge, so quietly that hardly a ripple is left. At other times they plunge downward. During the breeding season, divers are found on ponds, lakes or on slow-moving rivers, but they migrate in winter to coastal waters to the south of the breeding range.

While feeding, divers stay under for a minute at the most, most dives lasting only 10–20 seconds, but if alarmed they can stay under longer and dive to great depths. One was caught in a fish net below 200 ft. While underwater, divers swim with their feet, using their wings only as stabilisers.

Divers can only take off from the water, and then only after a long run. The wings are small for the size of the body, but divers fly powerfully once aloft and have been clocked at 60 mph. Landing is spectacular; the diver circles the pool or river on rapidly beating wings, then glides down at a steep angle. As it skims towards the water it lowers its feet and slides to a halt with spray thrown up on either side.

Robert Burton

△ *Typical diver nest, with chick on the runway to the water and an egg hatching out in the nest.*
▷ *Great northern diver or common loon on its nest, built of decaying vegetation.*
▽ *Great northern diver family in convoy, with one chick hitching a ride on its parent's back.*

Pamela Harrison

The black-throated or Arctic diver represents the two smaller divers, which have greyish instead of blackish heads.

The cry of the northlands

No one who has heard the eerie call of a diver ever forgets it; it is a symbol of their wild but beautiful northern homeland. It is impossible to describe this call except poetically. The red-throated diver has been described as calling like the 'wail of a lost spirit, echoing and re-echoing around the hills', while the blood-curdling wails of the great northern divers have been sometimes mistaken for the howls of a wolf. According to the Norse people, if divers flew overhead calling, they were following souls to heaven.

Do divers spoil fishing?

Divers eat mainly fish, both freshwater and marine, such as sand-eel, gudgeon, goby and the young of larger fish such as flounder, trout and perch. One American diver was found with a 15in. pike-perch stuck in its gullet. Crustaceans, molluscs and some vegetation are also eaten.

Sometimes fishermen complain that divers spoil the fishing, but except when they are in their winter flocks, divers are very unlikely to have any effect on fish populations, although they do on occasion become tangled in lines and nets. On the Inland Sea of Japan, divers drive fish into compact schools, where the fishermen can easily net them.

The diver 'slipway'

Courtship takes place on the water, with divers chasing each other, either splashing, half-flying across the surface, or swimming with body partly-submerged and neck held out stiffly. Mating may take place on the nest or in the water, both birds submerging

for part of the time.

The nest is usually a depression in a hummock near the water's edge, but the great northern diver sometimes builds a heap of decaying vegetation. A 'slipway' may be formed as the divers shuffle to and fro. Incubation of the 2 or 3 eggs is shared by the parents. The black fluffy chicks emerge after a month and soon take to the water. At first they cannot dive and can swim only weakly; the ripples from the slightest breeze keep them pinned against the bank. They often ride on their parents' backs or retire to the nest when tired, but soon they are able to dive well, disappearing underwater for 6 – 7 seconds if danger threatens. The chicks grow rapidly and their diving ability improves apace. Their parents continue to feed them for 7 weeks, and they can fly at 10 – 11 weeks.

Dangers to the chicks

If a diver is disturbed on the nest it 'freezes' with neck stretched low, and if further disturbed it slips quietly off the nest and into the water, submerging and surfacing some distance away. So unless an enemy sees the diver leave the nest it will not know there is a nest there unless it comes across the camouflaged eggs by accident. Foxes, mink, otters, crows, skuas and herring gulls are probable enemies of divers, especially of their eggs and chicks.

Prophesying weather

In the Shetland Islands, the red-throated divers are called rain geese, and are said to foretell rain as their cry 'we're a' weet,

waur wedder' (We're all wet, worse weather) rings out over the lochs. There is also a saying connecting the movements of divers and the weather. On the Island of Foula, the most isolated of the Shetland group, where divers still nest on Luimisheddon (Old Norse, *loma-tjorn* — tarn of the diver) the saying is remembered as:

'When the rain goose goes to the hill
All the fishermen go where they will.
When the rain goose goes to the sea
All the fishermen go to the lee.'

Unfortunately, this cannot be taken so literally as to provide a local forecast to rival that of the Meteorological Office, but it is based on reasonable fact. In another version the second line runs 'You can go to the haaf when you will'. The haaf is the fishing season, lasting from mid-May to early August and coinciding with the diver's nesting season. So the old saying boils down to little more than that it is safe to go fishing during the diver's breeding season, but when they leave for their winter quarters at sea the weather is likely to be nasty.

class	**Aves**		
order	**Gaviiformes**		
family	**Gaviidae**		
genus & species	*Gavia immer* great northern diver		
	G. adamsii white-billed diver		
	G. arctica black-throated diver		
	G. stellata red-throated diver		